THE POPE FROM THE GHETTO

✦ CLUNY CLASSICS ✦

The Pope from the Ghetto

THE LEGEND OF THE FAMILY OF PIER LEONE

A Novel

Gertrud von Le Fort

Translated from the German
DER PAPST AUS DEM GHETTO
by Conrad M. R. Bonacina

❁

CLUNY
Providence, Rhode Island

Cluny Media edition, 2021

This Cluny edition is a republication of *The Pope from the Ghetto*,
originally published by Sheed & Ward in 1935.

This edition is published under license of Preservation Books,
a non-profit corporation dedicated to promoting
the fair use, appreciation, and preservation of great works.

For more information regarding this title,
please write to info@clunymedia.com, or to
Cluny Media, P.O. Box 1664, Providence, RI 02901

⁂   ⁂   ⁂

VISIT US ONLINE AT WWW.CLUNYMEDIA.COM

ISBN: 978-1952826580

Cover design by Clarke & Clarke
Cover image: Egon Schiele, *Crescent of Houses* (*The Small City V*),
oil on canvas, 1915
Courtesy of Wikimedia Commons

I

THIS history lies scattered in many fragments, large and small, of the golden city of Rome: where it is still possible to read them, they have been pieced together, and where it is no longer possible to do so, Night writes in the spaces between.

✻

PETRUS Leonis was the son of Baruch Leonis; but Baruch Leonis was the son of Chanoch ben Ezra, whom the people falsely call Benedictus Christianus.

This is the story that is told: Chanoch ben Ezra lived in the years of the great earthquakes. At that time many Jews in Rome met with a violent death because they were believed, by the exercise of their magic arts, to have called up the powers of hell in order to destroy the city which had subjugated Jerusalem in days gone by. (For, as we all know, there is a prophecy of St. Benedict which says that Rome can be destroyed only by the power of the elements, and that is why the Romans act more foolishly and are thrown into a wilder state of panic at the slightest trembling of the earth than at sight of a whole army of barbarians.)

As had been done six centuries before, in the time of the great Plague, the image of Christ in the Holy Father's Chapel (the one that was painted by St. Luke) was carried in solemn procession through all the streets of the city for the space of three days. At the moment when the head of the procession with its golden cross was issuing from the shadows of the narrow streets out on to the white bridge over the Tiber, which is called the Pons Senatorum, the earth suddenly shook again with such violence that the bridge collapsed into the river before the very eyes of the procession which was about to cross it. A terrible panic arose among those taking part: some fell to the ground in sheer terror and lay as if dead; others called on the saints; others again bethought them of the Jews. "Up, at them!" they cried, "let us punish them with their own crimes!" The bearers hurriedly stuck the shafts of their crosses and banners into the ground, and seizing stones from the wreckage of the bridge, made a rush for the Jewish quarter. (For the Pons Senatorum is, as everyone knows, the next bridge above the Pons Judaeorum, near to which dwell many Jews on both sides of the river.)

It happened that among those who fell into the hands of the frenzied mob was the aforementioned Chanoch ben Ezra, a venerable old man who, terrified by the earthquake, had rushed out of his house. He tore himself from their grasp, and fled bleeding and disfigured, and with his clothes in rags, to the back of the procession, which the priests had managed to keep under control. There, where as under a wall of gold and snow, the image of Christ the King was advancing, the people were still praying as the Jew, pelted by the stones of his pursuers, burst in. On a sudden the cry went up, at first more in distress than in rage: "A sacrilege! A sacrilege!" Chanoch ben Ezra, borne along more by the fear of death than by his aged limbs, had broken through the white and gold rampart of the priestly dalmatics, and sank streaming with blood at the feet of the Pope.

With the image of Christ in his hand, the latter, sunk in meditation and almost crushed by the gold of his tiara and cope, looking himself like a statue and wholly absorbed in the service of the holy image, involuntarily took a step backwards; but the old man in his despair pressed forward with trembling knees and hid his head under the purple cope of the Pontiff.

It was rumored later that by a sudden illumination the Holy Father had recognized in the face of this old Jew, hidden though it was in his cope, the prototype in the likeness of which the Creator had once molded the countenance of St. Peter, and that this was the reason why he gave the helpless old man his protection. But the truth was just the reverse: the Jew and the Roman people were at this hour, for the first time after many years, to behold again in the countenance of their Pope the apostolic majesty of St. Peter.

The time was still recent when the turbulent family of the Tusculans had subjected the Holy See to their impious domination, and this Pope was one of the first who issued from the great ecclesiastical reform of Cluny. He beheld no vision, but he remembered the law of Christian mercy and the statutes of his holy predecessors of earlier times, who had proclaimed by stern decree the inviolability of the Jewish people, that they might be converted, or failing that, also bear witness in their own way to Christ dead upon the Cross.

At first the crowd dared not lay hands on the sacred vestments, but shouted to the Pope to throw back his cope and deliver the evil-doer into their hands, that the earthquake might cease. Already sinister voices were heard clamoring in the background and asking whether the hands of those who had risen against Benedict IX had grown withered!

The Holy Father felt his heart tremble, for he was only a man, and the mob was out of hand. Recent years had seen more than one Pope maltreated by the laity, nay, suffer a violent death at their hands. There were many too who had a grievance against him because he refused to tolerate the sale of ecclesiastical offices. Only he carried in his hands the image of Him who died also for the Jews, and he was resolved for his part also to die, if need be, for this Jew. Without answering a word, he kept his gaze fixed on the holy image raised in his hands, merely lifting this a little higher, so that it was visible to the crowd but at the same time concealed his face. And thus they stood, the two of them, facing the raging world, the Pope in his tiara, and the aged Jew clinging to his feet, as though rooted there.

The mob hesitated: the Pope himself they would have attacked, but the sacred image in his hands inspired them with fear. They did not retire, however, but stood their ground threateningly, like a wall of flesh and silence which might at any moment fall in and bring death in its fall.

Suddenly the voice of the Jew made itself heard beneath the Holy Father's cope, crying aloud for mercy: "I believe in God the Father Almighty, Creator of heaven and earth!"

Whereupon the Pope still announcing the holy message in his hands, continued in quiet tones (but it was as though his voice were passing into that of the man at his feet): "And in Jesus Christ, His only Son, Our Lord, who was conceived by the Holy Spirit."

For a moment the silence around was so breathless that one almost seemed to hear it; then it gave way to loud shoutings: "The Jew confesses the Credo! The Jew is converted! A miracle at the feet of the Holy Father!" The wall shook: the people fell on their knees. In the respite thus gained, some clerics got the fainting Jew safely out of the way.

WHEN evening came the opinion was being expressed everywhere in Rome that the earthquake would not be repeated, as one of the Jews who had provoked it had by a sudden miraculous illumination been converted to Christ. It was also asserted that Chanoch ben Ezra had that same day been baptized in the name of Benedict, and the Romans who in the morning had tried to stone the Jew, were now storming at the gate of the various monasteries where the happy neophyte was rumored to be in hiding, in order that they might kiss the hands of the man who, as they now believed, had saved their city from the scourge of the earthquake. But everywhere they found only the Papal guards, who refused to give them any information.

THE conversation that took place between Chanoch ben Ezra and the Holy Father:

This was some years later, in the days when the Romans, incited by the greed of their captains, were threatening to drive the Holy Father out of the city if he persisted in prohibiting the traffic in ecclesiastical offices. (For it was the sons of the nobility who reaped the profits of this simoniacal plague.) Large sums of money were being distributed by the simoniacs among the credulous masses; but the Holy Father sat with empty pockets in the Leonine City, with no other protector than the treacherous sword of Cencius Frangipane, who was at this very moment bargaining with the enemy over the price of that sword.

This was the Cencius Frangipane whom the people nicknamed Hercules, because of the mighty strength of his big blond body, for Lombard blood flowed in his veins.

Often before, Cencius had sought to advance his fortunes through the Holy See, just as the other families used the simoniacs to advance theirs, for he believed (as many before him had done) that to protect a Pope was to hold him in one's power. But since he did not act from motives of duty or loyalty, or from any comprehension of the divine mission of Holy Church, he soon fell away in time of need. The Holy Father was well aware of this; and so it was that at a time when the anointed protector of the Church of Christ on earth, the Emperor with his consecrated sword, reposed in the Cathedral of Speyer, and when the Empire was waiting for his son to attain his majority, the Bride of Christ had to content herself with the doubtful shield of a lowly vassal....

When the Jew entered, he fell on his face in humble obeisance. He then placed before the Holy Father two heavy money-bags filled with gold, and asked if he might be allowed to rise so that he could go and fetch the others, which he had left with his servant outside, as they were more than he could carry all at once.

The young Pope, who had the keen ascetic face of the typical monk, asked in astonishment why this money was brought to him now, since it was not the time when the Jews usually paid their tribute.

Chanoch ben Ezra: "But it is the time when Your Holiness is in need."

"And what is that to you, Jew?" asked the Pope, in whom the mere sight of money was apt to arouse a feeling of repulsion, so embittered was he become through his struggle with the shameless simoniacs.

The Jew: "I am Chanoch ben Ezra whom Your Holiness once protected under your cope from the raging mob."

"Not I, my son, not I," the Pope quickly put in, "but Christ, in whose place I stand."

The Jew was disconcerted and remained silent. One could see how his whole body writhed; for he did not wish to hear anything about the Incarnate Godhead on the Cross: his gratitude was meant only for the justice which the Holy Father had rendered him as man.

The Pope read his mind with sorrow; but at the same time he recognized the noble humanity of the Jew. "Chanoch," he said, "you have a grateful soul, and that is a rare thing in this world! So help me God, I would have been better pleased if you had brought me your soul instead of this purse!"

"His purse *is* his soul," whispered Cencius Frangipane, who was in attendance on the Pope.

"No!" replied the Pope in swift reproof, "this purse is his fidelity!" But the Jew perceiving that the Holy Father was well disposed towards him, and filled with the desire to show his gratitude, hastened to remark with a gesture of humility:

"It is true, Holy Father, that we Jews, as my lord here says, love money all too much, but you Romans love it even more than we do!"

"Whether they love it more than you do, I do not know," sighed the Pope, "but love it they certainly do. Yes, they love money so much that if Rome could find a buyer, they would offer themselves for sale."

"Buy them, Holy Father, buy them!" said the Jew with blunt candor. "For if you do not buy them, they will hurl you from the throne and elect a Pope who will once again put the Church benefices up for sale."

The young Pope gave the Jew a pensive look full of melancholy. "What humility must that man practice here upon earth whom Jesus Christ has chosen to represent Him!" he murmured.

But Frangipane, seeing that the balance was turning in favor of the Jew's counsel, and trembling for the price of his own treachery, cried out angrily:

"Miserable Jew, are you proposing to sell the noble city of the Romans, as your cursed Judas sold Our Lord?"

For the second time the Pope showed his displeasure: "Show me one of the coins that the Jew has brought," he said sharply and with a touch of malice in his voice. This was done. "Whose is the image stamped thereon, Cencius Frangipane?" asked the Pope. "Is it the likeness of the Jew?"

Frangipane, purple with rage: "It is the monogram of the City of Rome."

The Pope: "Then render to Rome the things that are Rome's and to God the things that are God's!"

And thus it came to pass in the workings of divine Providence that, through the gratitude of a miserable Jew, the Holy Father in his great fight for the liberty of the Church of Christ was saved from the hands of the traitorous Romans.

THE chronicle relates:

And God blessed the fidelity of Chanoch ben Ezra. He became rich as no Jew or any other person in the city of Rome before him had ever been. Indeed, it was as if all the gold with which he had come to the help of the Holy Father at that time had been moved to increase a hundredfold, even though he did not charge more than the usual and authorized rate of interest thereon. (For it is not with the Jews as it is with the Christians, for whom the taking of interest is forbidden by Holy Church.)

It was this blessing, they say, which caused the son of Baruch, otherwise known as Baruch ben Baruch, whom the people call Baruch Leonis (because of his splendid new mansion on the Porta Leone), likewise to place his services at the disposal of Holy Church; though he did this not out of gratitude, like his father, for Baruch Leonis was known everywhere as a usurer who never undertook anything save for the profit it brought him.

This is the sort of man Baruch Leonis was: just as with his naked hand he could tell more surely and subtly than the most delicate gold

scales whether a piece of money was of standard weight or ever so
slightly debased, so with the keen faculties of his mind could he distinguish between the good and bad coins in the currency of world events,
and estimate to a nicety the weight of the various forces in play there.
Baruch Leonis, in other words, was a shrewd man who saw clearly that
the day of the all-powerful captains in Rome was over, and that the only
way to prosper in the future was to throw in one's lot with the Holy See.

THE chronicle relates:

One day the great captains of the city came booted and spurred to
the carpeted mansion of the rich Baruch Leonis and asked him for a
large loan. They were at that time organizing a secret rebellion against
the Holy Father, for they were now in a state of alarm not merely on
account of their sinful simoniac gains, as formerly, but also on account of
the Patarini. (This was the name given to the riff-raff of the lower quarters of Milan who had broken into the houses of the simoniac priests
and threatened to beat to death the captains who protected them.)

Baruch Leonis (he was busy just then counting his money; it flowed
through his large bony hands like a silver brook over pebbly boulders): If
the captains needed the money for the defence of the Pope, he was ready
to advance it to them, since he knew that it would then be consecrated
to a matter for which the Christian world was ready at all times to rise
up like a wave.

The captains were not a little astonished at Baruch's reply, for they
themselves still believed that one straight blow delivered at the great
reform of Holy Church from outside would make the reform collapse
of itself, since it was manifestly fighting against the natural course and
usages of the world, and that thereafter everything would be as it was
before.

From that day forward, so it is reported, Johannes Frangipane (he
was the son of that Cencius who had always been so ready to betray his
trust) did not desert the Holy Father so frequently, and for a brief while
Holy Church was really able to rely on his protection.

THE chronicle relates:

And Baruch Leonis became as powerful as his father before him had been rich. When he rode through the streets, all the beggars and cripples saluted him with the title of "Illustrious Consul and Senator of the Romans," for in the number of men-at-arms and gorgeously attired slaves who attended him he could rival and even surpass the first captains of the city. (And he lent a willing ear to this form of acclamation.) Johannes Frangipane, who now treated him as an equal, was a constant visitor at his house. The Jew's name was ever on his lips: Baruch Leonis agrees, or Baruch Leonis does not agree, or Baruch Leonis advises this or that. But this was only another way of saying: Baruch Leonis is giving money for a project, or he refuses to do so. But Baruch Leonis always gave money when Frangipane supported the Pope.

People in Rome suddenly recalled to mind the old legend about Benedictus Christianus: some declared that the son had received baptism at the same time as the father, and that his real name was Leo (after the Holy Father Leo IX), while others maintained that he was going to be baptized almost at once. But it was Frangipane who spread these reports. He himself always pretended to believe them, for he was afraid that the Holy Father, on whom he now seriously relied for the advancement of his fortunes, might otherwise find fault with him for associating so closely with an unbaptized Jew. The Romans, however, gave him willing echo; for, that a Jew might be rich and learned, they were ready to allow, but that he should also become a mighty captain of their city was a thing quite unheard of, and they could not reconcile themselves to such a possibility.

This was the condition of the Jews in Rome.

They now no longer had to endure the sufferings that befell them during the period of the great earthquake, for the Romans, save when they lose their heads, as during those dreadful days, still hold that their city is the capital of the universe, and that they have the power to confer the rights of citizenship on all the peoples of the earth. This thought is for them an intoxicating dream, in which they live over again the ancient glories of their vast heap of ruins. And hence also, all the Sovereign Pontiffs of the great Reform extended a protective hand over the little Jewish city on the banks of the Tiber. One saw its inhabitants go in and out unmolested, men and women with black hair and dark eyes like the other men and women around them (for in Rome only the captains are blond). Nevertheless they were not like the others, but seemed as strangers who had come from afar. And yet they had been settled in their quarters for more than a thousand years, that is to say, ever since their fathers and mothers had been led into captivity, what time the Temple treasure of Jerusalem was borne along in the triumph of Titus. Sometimes they remarked jokingly to each other that they were now without a doubt the oldest citizens of Rome (because of all the families that had flourished when they came, not a single one was still to be seen). But there was a note of sadness in their jesting, for not one of them when he stepped beyond the gates of Rome trod on his own piece of soil, but the corn in their granaries was bought corn, and the wine in their cellars was bought wine, and the flowers in the hair of their daughters were bought flowers. Only the money in their purses was their own money.

THE chronicle relates:

The Ruler of the Jewish community, to whom the current rumors were not unknown, felt obliged at last to demand from Baruch Leonis an explanation of his constant intercourse with the Christians. Baruch Leonis replied: "Our brethren in Andalusia and Cordova administer the crowns of kings and the scepters of caliphs, and their masters are grateful to them. Why should not Israel prosper in Rome as she prospers in Spain?"

Whereupon the Ruler, a humble man of deep piety: "My son, it is dangerous for Israel when her people prosper."

Baruch Leonis: "Are then the people of the Lord—praise be to Him—always to stand aside in this world?"

The Ruler: "How can a son of Israel speak so? Knowest thou not,

Baruch, what our masters teach: The Holy One—praise be to Him—
despised the high mountains and revealed Himself on lowly Sinai?"
Baruch Leonis: "But our masters also teach that it is better to be the
tail of the lion than the head of the fox." The Ruler: "My son, thy brothers and sisters place their hopes in the
God of their fathers—praise be to Him—and wilt thou place thine in
the children of Edom?"
Baruch Leonis with a smile: "No, but let them put theirs in me!"
But when the Ruler asked in shocked surprise if this meant that
Baruch was going to receive baptism, as was commonly reported, Baruch
gave forth a loud roar like a wounded bull. At this the Ruler and the two
witnesses who had accompanied him hurriedly left the room, pale with
fear at such an explosion of anger and pain, and so far as is known the
Synagogue never again deemed it necessary to admonish Baruch Leonis,
although the Frangipani and the people continued to invent tales of his
baptism.

THE chronicle relates:
The legends about Baruch Leonis only ceased when the great Arch-
deacon Hildebrand ascended the Papal throne. Using his despotic power
in the name of Christ, he succeeded for a while in bringing order to
the disordered world, and in assigning to each and all their rightful
place before God and man: the simoniac priests were banished from the
Church; men of holy lives were appointed to bishoprics; the Christians,
princes and people alike, were made to submit to their pastors, and the
Jews, while left unharmed, were kept strictly within the bounds of their
community. Henceforward Baruch Leonis was forbidden to have Christian slaves and retainers, for, said the Holy Father, it was not fitting that
the unbaptized should have power over the baptized; and at the same
time Frangipane was given to understand that it would become him
better as a knight of Holy Church, if he relied more on the protection
of Christ and less on the counsel and wealth of Baruch Leonis. Accordingly, Johannes Frangipane, who feared the stern Pope's anger, withdrew

from the society of his Jewish friend, and for a time one heard no more talk of the latter's influence, until one day it was learned that Baruch Leonis was dead and that his affairs and immense wealth had passed into the hands of his son.

THE son of Baruch Leonis.

This man was not a usurer like his father, but a man of quality, dignified in his bearing and conduct, who at once restored his father's usurious gains. In his community he was known to be a faithful observer of the Law in all its details. Nevertheless it is common knowledge that before long the Synagogue also became anxious about him, even though it could not say of him that he mixed himself up in the affairs of the Christians. But it seems that it was precisely the fact that he did not do so that gave rise to this anxiety (for the son of Baruch was, as everyone said, a far cleverer man than his father). However, the Synagogue did not arrange to have him questioned and admonished as his father had been, but it arranged for him to marry Miriam, the daughter of the Rabbi Nathan ben Jechiel, who was surnamed "The Stern." At that time, however, Miriam herself was not stern, she was only beautiful.

THE chronicle relates:

The Holy Father Gregory VII was at first unwilling to allow the son of Baruch Leonis to be enrolled among the catechumens, and when the deacon who had the care of these came to him to announce the joyful news of such an important new conversion, he curtly refused to see him. But at Holy Mass next day, he was seen to be weeping more bitterly than usual—this Pope could never offer up the Holy Sacrifice without tears— so that the Countess Matilda of Tuscany, who was staying in Rome at that time, could not but think of the day when the young German monarch, Henry IV, had feigned repentance at her mountain castle of Canossa, in order to obtain absolution. (For it was then becoming clear that the Salian's change of heart at Canossa was a mere pretence and that he had acted the penitent only as a means of saving his tottering throne;

he remained as much opposed to the liberties of Holy Church as were the miserable captains of Rome, although he desired to be consecrated Emperor.) The Holy Father had wept with equal bitterness during Mass that morning at the Castle of Canossa, and these tears had then given the Countess courage to plead for the excommunicated monarch. But today too her intercession was being sought, for she had given not only all her lands and possessions, but all the faculties of her soul as well into the hands of St. Peter, and the Apostle's successor put greater trust in her than in any other person on earth. Certain of the cardinals, however, were of opinion that the Holy Father was perhaps afraid lest the power of the dangerous and fickle captains would be unduly strengthened if the son of Baruch Leonis with his immense riches became allied with them by marriage, and that this was the secret reason why he refused his consent to the baptism.

OUR Holy Father Gregory VII and the Countess of Tuscany.

This Pope was small, and of poor physique: at his enthronement, the ample robes of his predecessor hung loosely over his puny shoulders, like crippled wings, but in his large eyes dwelt a ruler who was not of this world, and when he pronounced the name of Christ, the word rang out like the sound of a bell reaching to the ends of the earth.

The Holy Father to the Countess: "Daughter, are you still thinking of the days at Canossa?"

The Countess (her countenance was frail, but eloquent of courage like that of a young man; joy spoke therein, for she had sensed in advance what the Holy Father was thinking, and it was the endeavor of her pious zeal to divine him and understand him in all things): "Holy Father, today at the altar you wept as you did then."

The Holy Father: "But do you also know, daughter, why we wept?" Then, with his large eyes aflame: "You say that at Canossa, the Salian made the politician yield to the priest, but Christ is our witness: it was not the politician in us that strove against him in the beginning; on the contrary, it was the priest."

The Countess (her clear gaze now questioning his in sad humility, for she had hitherto believed what everyone else had believed): "Holy Father, your daughter is not in possession of your deepest thoughts."

He looked at her gently, for no one had the key to these. Then his expression changed, as if a veil were lifted from the chalice of his soul.

The Countess, in sudden awe, whispered: "At Canossa it had to do with the holiness of the Sacrament of Penance."

The Holy Father: "It had to do with the holiness of the Sacrament of Penance—it always has to do with the holiness of the Sacraments. Even when it is a question of politics, it concerns the honor of the Sacrament, for the ordination of our bishops is sacramental, and even the consecration of the Emperor is a holy thing for him. Always it concerns Christ alone! Yet at Canossa we could not protect the Sacrament; the formal rules given to us for the granting of absolution had been complied with, even though we knew in our heart that... For it is Christ's will, that He should suffer for the sins of this world unto the end of time."

Next morning the deacon, whom the Holy Father had previously sent away, received the following order: "Let the son of Baruch Leonis be enrolled among the catechumens, but let him be given time to prove himself."

This is how the future Petrus Leonis underwent his period of probation. (But the course it took did not turn out as the Holy Father had anticipated.)

There are still living among us enemies of Holy Church who assert that the great Pontiff Gregory VII was a sorcerer (just as they used to say it about Pope Silvester II in his time), an adept in the black magic, which they teach at the high school of the Infidels at Cordova. This rumor goes back to the days when the German Emperor Henry IV had come down upon us in order to wrest from the Holy Father at the point of the sword, the Investiture of the spiritual princes and the Imperial crown. At that time one saw in our city many a captain, who had once been a supporter of the simoniacs, transformed into a zealous reformer, and many a persecutor of the Patarini become a brother of the poor.

This wonderful unity was the work of our Holy Father Gregory, who brought it about solely through the power of his large eyes, and the way he pronounced the name of Jesus Christ among us. However, the scandalous talk about the Pope Magician did not spring from this wonderful concord, the like of which had never been seen in the city of Rome before that time, but it sprang from the granaries of corn with which the son of Baruch Leonis kept us nourished during the blockade, just as his forefather Joseph had once nourished the hungry Egyptians. For it was impossible to explain save through the agency of black magic—so say those who speak of the Pope Magician—how it was that our stores did not give out during the seven long months of the siege. Nevertheless they came to an end at last (just as our concord came to a lamentable end): our fierce hunger and our terrible weakness bear witness in favor of our Holy Father, had he need of any such witness: they were our last scraps of bread that we threw to the people to keep them quiet, while the Holy Father was being hurried away to the Moles Hadriani [the Castle of St. Angelo].

That flight took place, as we all know, in great haste and confusion, for when the tocsin was sounded on the left bank of the Tiber, our captains were still encamped in the Leonine City, imploring the Holy Father on their knees, to yield to the Salian's wishes and so save the city from disaster. But the Fourth Henry knew our Holy Father better than they did (for he knew him not indeed with his small, insolent eyes, but with his evil conscience, and this saw with penetrating glance).

He ordered his Saxons and Thuringians to break into the Leonine City, even before the Pope's *No* had been brought to him.

The Holy Father had to be forcibly lifted to a height of seven steps, so high lay the pile of corpses under the portico of St. Peter's. He passed over them on the arms of his fleeing rescuers, with calm face, praying in a loud voice for the poor souls of the slain. Behind him Johannes Frangipane threw himself with his followers across the street, and carved it in two with his sword. But this he could essay and accomplish only because he knew that on the other side of the Tiber, the son of Baruch

Leonis was standing on the threshold of his house (where abundance still reigned) distributing bread among the Romans, who were already gathered together in readiness to fall on Frangipane in the rear, for hunger had made them wild like the beasts of the forests. When they caught sight of the son of Baruch Leonis at the open door of his magnificent dwelling, they rushed towards his hands like wild cats; it was a miracle that they did not tear his limbs from his body.

Ever since that day there has been a saying current in Rome: to be united like the sword of the Frangipani and the purse of the Pier Leoni.

THE chronicle relates:

When our Holy Father Gregory VII lay dying at Salerno, and the cardinals, who had followed him out of the smoking Rome into exile, were gathered around him to receive his last instructions, they asked him among other things if he would allow them to depart from his stern injunctions in regard to the son of Baruch Leonis, and to grant the Jew baptism.

The Holy Father Gregory, his dying voice still strong as sounding brass: "We have not treated him more sternly than our own bishops: our Sacraments are not for sale."

Whereupon, one of the cardinals reminded the Holy Father how the son of Baruch Leonis had risked his life for him at the time of his flight.

The Holy Father Gregory: "In Rome, no one risks his life who has bread or gold in his hands."

Again the cardinal who had spoken before; he was an old man full of gentleness: "His life, not, Holy Father, but his hands; and they too mean something to a man!"

The Holy Father was then for a long time silent. At last he spoke; his voice was like a cracked bell, but the tone was not that of a dying man, but the same as that with which he had once pronounced the absolution of the Emperor Henry: "So be it. Let the son of Baruch Leonis receive baptism, but first let him be led once again through the burnt portico

of St. Peter's, and before the palace where our adversary sits enthroned."
(This was the impious heresiarch Guibert whom the Salian had installed
there.) "Then let him be told how we died, and see that they do not conceal from him a single one of our last words."

The Holy Father was here referring to the words: "I have always
loved justice and hated iniquity; therefore I die in exile." But he might
also have said: "Therefore I bear the crown of thorns of my Lord and
Savior."

When this message was brought to the son of Baruch Leonis—its
purport could only be fulfilled after they had begun to rebuild the portico of St. Peter's—he replied: "Henceforth no Pope must ever die in
exile." There were many who recalled to mind this answer later, when
our Holy Father Innocent II was compelled to flee to France before
the Cardinal Pier Leone, the same who became the schismatical Pope
Anacletus II.

ABOUT Miriam, mother of the schismatical Pope Anacletus II, and
daughter of the Rabbi Nathan ben Jechiel, whom they had married to
Petrus Leonis (henceforth the son of Baruch will be called by this name).

THE Jews of Rome relate:
She was known in her community as Miriam the Beautiful; it is in
her image that the stone statue of the Queen of Juda in the Cathedral of
Chartres was made. She had accompanied her man there on one of his
business journeys, for she loved him so much that she could never bear
to be parted from him. But he so loved her that he dared not speak to
her of his baptism, and she believed in his silence as in the holy Torah.
When it was bruited in the Jewish city that he had been received among
the catechumens, her father urged her to leave him. But Miriam smiled
into the silken veils her husband had given her: "I do not believe it, and
I will not believe it."

Whereupon the Rabbi: "Have you then never questioned your husband about his loyalty to Israel?"

Miriam, kissing the ring she wore on her finger, and which her husband had given her: "I have never questioned him, and I will not question him ever."

The Rabbi insisted: "But cannot you then see what all the world sees?"

Miriam, closing her eyes, as if she were closing them upon her happiness: "I have seen nothing, and I will not see anything."

The Rabbi then remained silent, for he could not believe that he had lost his daughter.

It is as a result of this conversation that the Jews hoped in the son of Baruch Leonis to the end.

THE Jews of Rome relate:

This was how Miriam the Beautiful came to be known as Miriam the Great. She was not so named because she was tall in stature and of a majestic appearance, but her soul was one of those of which it is written in the Book of Proverbs: "Who shall find a valiant woman? Far and from the uttermost coasts is the price of her." On the very day when Petrus Leonis and his two young sons by his first marriage were baptized at Saint Johannes in Fonte, Miriam tore off the marriage veils which covered her head. She then took from its press the bridal robe in which she had once stood beside her betrothed under the baldachin, and put it on. It rose upon her body like the swell of a wave, for her union had again been blessed for some months past. Only the crown which had encircled her radiant brow as bride she did not put on; but on the beauty of her uncovered head she strewed ashes. And thus, with the crown in her hand, like a dishonored bride who has not been joined in wedlock, and with the heavy step of a woman big with child, she made her way out through the horrified crowd of her husband's domestics, and went to the house of her father, the Rabbi Nathan ben Jechiel.

When Hannah Naemi, the Rabbi's sister, saw her, she knew at once what had happened: if Miriam returned with ashes on her head, it could mean only one thing, for until the day when this happened, she had not been a woman of strict piety, but rather a queen of luxury and vanity.

For many years past there had been much talk among the Jews of the golden shoes of the Senatrix Marozzia, which in an hour of sore need the Counts of Tusculum had sold to the son of the wealthy Baruch Leonis, and because she wore them Miriam had been bitterly slandered by the women of her people. But henceforth they only spoke of her luxurious tastes, in order to give greater luster to the fame of her renunciation.

Meanwhile Hannah Naemi had begun to utter wild lamentations, as is the custom of the Jews when one of their number falls victim to the snares of Edom. And immediately the women of the people poured out of the neighboring houses and surrounded Miriam with a concert of wailing. Only Miriam herself raised no cry, for she could not speak for sorrow. She had a mouth molded in the manner of the daughters of Zion, rather large, but lovely and dark like the petal of a rose. This, to be sure, she opened, but no sound issued therefrom; it was as if the cry had been frozen upon her lips and hung invisible in the air above the wailing women. And suddenly these, contrary to their custom and duty in such cases, became mute like her, for the feeling came upon them that their cries must pierce like arrows the heart of the afflicted woman whom they wished to solace with their wailing.

By this time Nathan ben Jechiel had been roused by the concourse before his house, and he also divined at once what had happened. As he stepped outside his door, he was already clutching his clothes convulsively with his hands, in order to rend them. Then Miriam, with all the weight of her body, fell down before him like a dark, humble stone. And when the Rabbi saw his child lying in ruined bridal attire at his feet, like one buried in grief, his face suddenly lit up with a fierce joy. Instead of rending his garments, he raised his hands and cried out with a loud voice: "Praised be the God of our fathers, who has preserved the heart of my child, and blessed be the heart of my child, who has kept the faith of our fathers!" After he had spoken these words, he placed his hands on Miriam's head, to bless her; and at that moment there passed through Miriam's body the first pains of coming child-birth, and they soothed the torment of her soul....

Scarcely had the infant uttered its first mewling, when a voice was heard in the street outside: "In the name of the illustrious Senator of the Romans, Petrus Leonis!" Hannah Naemi snatched up the tiny body as it lay there, still trembling and crumpled in its mother's blood, in order that they might dip it in its own blood, before its father's henchmen carried it off by force to be baptized. But it was too late, and instead of handing the infant to the Rabbi for him to slay it, Hannah Naemi ran with it straight into the arms of the men who had forced their way in.

These were led by Johannes Frangipane, who had just been holding in his huge blond fists the little black Jewish prince Obicione at the christening font, and his zeal for the golden star of this new rising family was such that he had brought with him the wet-nurse of his own child, that she might give her breast to the son of Petrus Leonis.

When the young and buxom nurse, protected by the outstretched sword of Frangipane, had made her way to Miriam's chamber, whither the terrified Hannah Naemi had rushed back with the child in her arms, she gave a cry of joy, for she saw how it stood with the young woman before her. She turned round to Frangipane and called out with a laugh: "Have a little patience, and in a moment you will have two Jewish babes to take to the christening font, instead of one."

But when she sat down to await the birth of the second child, it happened that the moans of the woman in travail suddenly ceased. And Miriam lay extended on the rack of her body for seven times seven hours, and concealed the second child, that was craving to see the light of day, in the stronghold beneath her heart, and guarded it with the power of her pains and of her will. And during these seven times seven hours Miriam the Beautiful became Miriam the Great, or rather she became Miriam the Grey-headed. Hannah Naemi saw how the ashes, which still lay upon her niece's head, seemed to grow darker and darker, because the hair beneath them was becoming lighter and lighter, as if in these seven times seven hours as many years were fleeting by: she saw it turn to grey, and she saw it become white like a fabric from which the last dye had been drained out.

And then, when Miriam had become very old like some ancient grandmother, she seemed to die, and the nurse of the Frangipani left her for dead.

THE Jews of Rome relate:

We know what follows from the chronicle of the Spanish Rabbi Ibn Mischal, who is called "The Torch of Israel," and who at that time was staying in Rome on his journey from Toledo to Jerusalem. His disciples tell of many visions that he had of the future.

When the Rabbi was introduced into Miriam's chamber, he prayed first of all on the threshold. Then he said, not in a very loud voice, but as if he were in the presence of someone in a light sleep: "Miriam, daughter of Nathan ben Jechiel, rejoice, for thy son whom Edom has ravished from thee, will rend the kingdom of Edom, which is called Christendom, from top to bottom, making it to return whence it came! Give forth then thy second child, for see, it is decreed: The weak shall lead the strong and the blind the one that sees, and the sister shall bring back the brother!"

Then Miriam gave birth to her second child, and this was that Trophäea, of whom so much was afterwards related. But Trophäea means "The Spoils of Victory." This, however, was not her real name, but was the name which the women of the Jewish city gave to the daughter of Miriam "because," said they, "this child has become the Trophy of her mother's victory."

II

———————◆———————

THE Jews of Rome relate: When the Rabbi Nathan ben Jechiel pronounced the major excommunication against Petrus Leonis, Miriam insisted on going with him to the Synagogue. At first Hannah Naemi raised an objection; an old married woman herself, she still wore mourning for her husband, and she regarded Miriam as a widow. But when she asked her niece whether her heart would not break, Miriam replied in a clear voice: "No, for my heart is already broken."

The Synagogue of the Jews had been built in an old Pagan temple whose rows of plain columns surrounded it like so many tall, slender candles. The rich men of the community had adorned the interior with gold and glittering mosaics, and silver lamps burned before the Holy of Holies. However, almost complete darkness reigned within, for next door to the Synagogue lived a Christian, and he had insisted on the windows on his side being walled up. As a child, Miriam had always been afraid of the dark Synagogue, but today she feared only the lights which the men carried in their hands, so as to put them out at the moment when the Rabbi pronounced the words of excommunication upon Petrus Leonis. She closed her eyes to the lights, and it was only when they blew *Truha* and the last light was extinguished that she opened them again, and then a great joy was born in her soul, as if she had been betrothed for a second time, and this time to the destiny of Israel, her people.

THE Jews of Rome relate:

And Miriam remained in the home of her father Nathan ben Jechiel, and assisted Hannah Naemi in the work of the household just as she had done before her marriage. While she was still stretched on her bed, the Rabbi had thought that he might have to send her away secretly to their co-religionists in another city, in order to save her child from its father. But after her recovery, he was able to calm his fears, for no one could suspect the new Miriam of being the mother of a new-born infant, and therefore that the child could belong to Petrus Leonis.

"Woman, you have a learned and famous son," said strange Jews to her, when they stayed at Nathan ben Jechiel's house, on their pilgrimage to Jerusalem. But to Nathan ben Jechiel they said: "Your mother, Rabbi, looks frailer than is usual in a woman of her years."

And Miriam regretted the loss of her youth and beauty as little as she mourned her husband. When Hannah Naemi, who had once sighed so much over her vanity, now tried to console her by saying that neither age nor suffering could ever destroy the natural nobility of her features, she seemed not to care and said nothing, or merely smiled down upon the child at her breast.

MIRIAM and her child.

Miriam used to lull her child to sleep by crooning to it the ancient hymns of her people, those in which the waters of Babylon still murmur their plaints. Formerly she could never bear to listen to these songs, as they sounded so sad; but now she loved them beyond all others that anyone could sing. Her voice had remained young, and she sang these mournful chants like hymns of triumph, as though all the sorrow therein were only the expectancy of a mighty victory.

This was the song of Miriam based on the words of the Prophet:

"Oh, that I had enough water in my head!
Oh, that my eyes were fountains!
I would weep day and night for the lost sons of my people!

For the sake of Zion I may not be silent and for Jerusalem's sake I
may not stay in my house,
Until Justice shall rise like a shining light and my redemption shall
take fire like a torch!"

As the child grew older, it tried to mingle its little voice with that
of its mother, at first only in a sort of babble, and then with single words
half-formed in childish fashion. Our old women say that Miriam's child
learned to pronounce the word "Jerusalem" before the name of its own
mother.

MIRIAM's child:

The little Trophäea had fine eager little hands which were always
touching and feeling things, and her intelligence was as lively as the
soaring of a young bird. All the aspects of the world about them, of
which she spoke to the child, Miriam immediately recognized again in
her eyes, delicately embedded there as in dark velvet. (But always it was
only the images evoked in her soul by her mother's words.) Often she
took her with her to that part of the Tiber bank which is known as "The
White Bank," because ever since the time of the great earthquake the
ruins of the Pons Senatorum have lain there. Also one can see from this
point the scattered remains of a vast marble forest stretching from the
Palatine Hill down to the bottom of the valley. On the crest of the hill
the growth of columns was still quite thick: a number of ancient trunks
stood there in rows, tall and erect. Others as in a primeval forest lay
in tumbled confusion, one on top of the other, or leaning against each
other. From some the foliage had departed, but it decked the tops of
many like a pride of snow. When the northern barbarians came to Rome
for the coronation of their Emperors, this sight reminded them of the
winter forests of their homeland.

The little Trophäea, tenderly in the direction of the marble forest:
"White! White!" Then (as if she could really see what her mother had
described to her): "Is that the forest of Jerusalem?"

The child spoke unceasingly of Jerusalem, so deeply had her mother's songs sunk into her soul. In order to still her curiosity, Miriam took her one day along the city wall to the Lateran Palace, where, it is said, in the Basilica (which the Christians call "of the Savior") two columns of the Temple are preserved which, each year on the day when the Holy City fell, drop sweat and tears.

Miriam in awed tones: "Inside there stand columns of our Temple."

The child: "Yes, I see them! Oh, how beautiful are our columns!"

Miriam in astonishment: "You see them? But the doors are closed!"

The child, naively: "But can one not see through closed doors?"

Whereupon Miriam dared not question her further.

THE Jews of Rome relate:

The Spanish Rabbi Elchanan (he was a disciple of Ibn Mischal) journeyed seven times from Toledo to Jerusalem and from Jerusalem back to Toledo, and on each of these pilgrimages he put up at the house of Nathan ben Jechiel. He took with him a sack, which was empty when he left Toledo, but which, on his return home from Jerusalem, bent the back of his mule with its weight.

"Look at the sly Spaniard who never lets his sack out of his hands," jeered the Romans, for they thought the Rabbi was so avaricious that he would not trust his treasure even to his own servant who rode behind him. But among the Jews of Rome the story went that Elchanan was bringing from Jerusalem to Spain the jewels of the Tombs of the Kings, and even that they were going to establish a new kingdom of Israel. (For ever since Baruch Leonis had said that the Spanish Jews administered the scepters of kings and caliphs, many of our folk believed this.)

On one occasion, while Elchanan was taking food with Nathan ben Jechiel, and the sack, covered with the Rabbi's great white travelling cloak, was lying in the dark passage outside the door of the dining-room, some Jewish men and women from the street slipped inside, in order to feel it. It was hard and stretched tight and looked as if the weight of its contents might burst the covering. On one side it stuck out in a sharp point which glittered like the sparkle of a small stone.

A poor man with hungry voice: "There are indeed bars of gold inside!"

A woman, in whispered awe: "No, it is the crown arrived already—I feel its sharp edges."

But suddenly the Rabbi issued from the door.

THE Rabbi Elchanan.

The Rabbi Elchanan had a nose pointed and curved like a Saracen blade from Damascus. As he came out of the door, his long narrow face was so pale that it was as if the blade was leaping out of an ivory sheath. The Rabbi Elchanan (for he had heard everything the people said): "I will show you the treasures of Israel and the crowns of your Spanish brothers!" Thereupon he opened the sack, and behold, there fell out a cloud of the fine, white dust of Jerusalem, which the Rabbi had fetched in order to lay it beneath the heads of the sons of Israel, when they sink into the grave.

The onlookers were dumbfounded, and remained silent; only the little Trophäea clapped her hands with joy, crying: "Why, I see the crown of King David! The Rabbi Elchanan has taken it out of his sack!"

When Hannah Naemi heard the child shouting with joy, she leaned her head against the door post and wept bitterly. But Miriam, who stood behind her, smiled.

THE Jews of Rome relate:

Sometimes Hannah Naemi tried, tenderly and discreetly, to speak to Miriam about the eyes of her child, for she and the Rabbi had known for a long time that the little Trophäea was blind. But Miriam seemed unable to grasp what she said.

Hannah Naemi to her brother: "She has no strength left, to meet this new blow; she has already suffered too much, she has become a weak woman again like the rest of us."

Whereupon the Rabbi: "The worst is not when a woman bends

under her weakness." (This, Hannah Naemi did not understand; later she understood it.)

But Miriam did not bend under her weakness, but it was with her as formerly before her husband's baptism, when she had said to her father: "I do not believe it, and I will not believe it." For Miriam thought of her son day and night, and all her hope in life hung on her daughter, of whom Ibn Mischal had prophesied that she would bring him back. But at this time all the songs of her people were silent on her lips, as if a stone sealed her pure voice.

THE Jews of Rome relate:

Hannah Naemi was healthy and robust for her years, only occasionally a flow of blood rushed to her head, so that everything grew dark before her eyes. One day when she had just taken fire from the hearth, in order to light the Sabbath candles in the dining-room, she was suddenly overtaken by one of these attacks of giddiness.

Hannah Naemi in the dark vestibule between the kitchen and the dining-room: "Help me, somebody, let someone come and lead me!"

At once Miriam's child sprang forward and wanted to take her hand.

Hannah Naemi, terrified because of the flaming brand she was carrying: "No, child, not you, not you! Call your mother!"

The child, without suspecting anything: "Why not me, auntie dear? Do you think I cannot see?"

Then Hannah Naemi wept bitter tears; she commended the flame in her hands to her guardian angel, and allowed the child to lead her into the dining-room. There the table stood ready for the meal, covered with fresh napery and furnished with the Sabbath dishes and the branched candlestick for the seven sacred lights. By it, in festive raiment, stood the Rabbi and Miriam, waiting in an attitude of devotion for Hannah Naemi to light the candles.

Hannah Naemi, gazing at Miriam (for she could now see quite clearly again), sighed within her: Oh, you poor thing, now that your child has guided my steps, you will close your mind more than ever to its fate! But as the glow from the flame spread itself over the faces, she saw in Miriam's pallor her mouth tremble, as though a flower were trying to open under the snow. And suddenly, with faltering step, Miriam went up to her little daughter, fell down on her knees before her, and grasped her two shoulders with her hands.

Miriam, with all the strength she could muster: "Tell me, child, can you see me or not?"

The child, fervently: "Yes, I see my darling mother."

Miriam pressing her withered face against the child's temples: "What do I look like, my own precious one?"

The child: "My mother is young and beautiful." Then Miriam burst into tears for the first time since the day of her husband's baptism. Everyone in the house of Rabbi Nathan ben Jechiel had come to believe that Miriam could no longer weep. Hannah Naemi put her arms gently round her and tried to comfort her; but Miriam raised herself and cried out with a loud voice: "The Lord be praised! Praise be to Him! Praise be to Him for all eternity!" But in this cry there was a wild note of jubilation, as of one transported in ecstasy or under the influence of wine, so that Hannah Naemi began to fear for her niece.

Hannah Naemi (she now understood her brother): "Bow your will, Miriam, yes, you must humble yourself, or your mind will give way! Cry, let the tears come!"

Miriam: "Why should I humble myself? The Lord has raised me up! Why should I weep? The Lord Himself has consoled me!"

Hannah Naemi (she thought her niece's mind had already given way): "Oh, Miriam, the mind of the Lord is inscrutable; give way, humble your heart, I beg of you, let the tears come!"

Miriam: "No, the mind of the Lord is made manifest! Or do you think that He who fulfilled the first promise of His servant will not also fulfill all the other promises of His servant?"

Then Hannah Naemi also remembered that Ibn Mischal had said: "The blind shall lead the one that sees." And she was amazed that until that moment not one of them had given thought to these words.

From this day Miriam believed with unshakable faith in the prophecy of Ibn Mischal.

MIRIAM'S song, when she knew that her child was blind (after the words of the Prophet):

> "Thou shalt no more have the sun for the light of day neither shall
> the brightness of the moon enlighten thee.
> But the Lord shall be unto thee for an everlasting light, and the
> days of thy mourning shall be ended!"

THE Jews in Rome relate:

And Miriam brought up her child in the hope which she herself drew from her blindness. Long before the little Trophäea knew who her brother was and who she herself was, that is to say, before she knew that there were such things as Jews and Christians, she knew that she would one day take her brother by the hand and lead him back to his mother, or, as her mother said, to the religion of his fathers.

One day a Jewish woman was passing by the house of Petrus Leonis (at the point where it falls like a tall jagged rock upon the "White Bank"), when she saw the little Trophäea standing in front of the steep wall, and knocking with her eager groping little fingers low down against the bare masonry.

The woman asked her what strange game she was playing.

The child replied: "The game is called going into the house of Petrus Leonis."

The woman to whom this happened, afterwards declared that the child had been knocking at the precise spot in the house of Petrus Leonis where, as everyone knows, lies the chapel.

THE House of Petrus Leonis.

The Jews of Rome relate:

Immediately after his baptism, Petrus Leonis built a chapel on to his house, and in addition he erected three majestic towers in order to show that he now belonged in very truth to the great captains of the City. The towers rose up close by the quarters of the Pons Judaeorum, upon which they frowned so defiantly that one might have thought they had been built either to threaten or to protect these. One of them, whose mighty roots plunged their ramifications into the ancient theater of Marcellus, was provided with a small balcony, which hung down from the massive structure of the tower like a little stone basket. When Miriam sat playing with her child on the "White Bank," she always looked up at this balcony, for she hoped to see her little son there. "She waits for him as if he were the Messiah," said the women of the Jews—they said it reverently, without disturbing Miriam. Hannah Naemi herself would have rubbed the skin off her old hands with work, rather than call her niece, when the latter sat waiting for the distant view of her son. From time to time the boy did actually appear on the balcony accompanied by his little brothers and sisters and his stepmother. (For Petrus Leonis had married again after his baptism, namely Donna Bona of the family of the Bericisi, and most of his children were hers.)

Donna Bona was tall and fair, but her children all resembled her two stepsons, Obicione and Guido and Miriam's little son as well. For the dark blood of Israel, old though it may be (so say we Jews), is stronger than that of the blond races; the Lord wills it so in order that His people may subsist through the day of their dispersion. Miriam was able to distinguish her son only because the old Rachel never left his side. But Rachel was recognized by Miriam through the melody of the song that she sang.

About Rachel, Miriam's old nurse: she was called "the mysterious daughter," by which was meant: of the Law.

The Jews of Rome relate:

At the time of his baptism, Petrus Leonis had given his servants both male and female the choice of leaving his service or following him to the baptismal font. And Rachel allowed the holy water to be poured over her, because she could not bear to be parted from Miriam's little son; for she had loved Miriam with the tenderness of a mother.

THE chronicle relates:

Though she was now an old woman, Rachel still possessed beautiful, even teeth; they were almost as white as the baptismal robe she was told to put over her. As she knelt on the threshold of the chapel where the priest was to baptize her, and the latter asked her: "What do you desire from Holy Church?" instead of an answer he met with a low grinding sound, harsh and bitter, like a sobbing with gnashing of teeth, and looking at her, he saw that Rachel was foaming at the mouth. He thought that the demons of her people were making a last effort to possess her, and ordered her to kiss the flagstones of the chapel. She obeyed him with such violence that blood flowed from her lips. He took this as a sign of her humility, and she then became sufficiently calm to be able to reply to him. He therefore baptized her without further hesitation. But afterwards, at the door of the chapel, when the infant, whose nurse she was going to be, was placed in her arms and she smiled for joy, one saw that her teeth were all broken, as if instead of kissing the stones of the chapel, she had bitten them.

It was Rachel's baptism which gave rise to the opinion, held here and there among the Jews, that Petrus Leonis likewise had only made a pretence of letting himself be baptized.

THE chronicle relates:

When the little boy Petrus grew old enough to dispense with Rachel's care, it was no longer by his nurse that Miriam recognized him, but by his little red coat, which was cut in a special way in imitation of the dress worn by young clerics. For Petrus Leonis had consecrated the son of Miriam to Holy Church at the baptismal font itself, in the fulness of his joy and gratitude, so it was said, at seeing his child's soul so happily rescued from the hands of the Jews. The boy, like his father, had been christened Petrus after the holy Apostle, but in the palace he always went by the name of "the little Cardinal." This name, however, did not, any more than the little red coat, owe its suggestion to Petrus Leonis, but to Donna Bona, his wife. Petrus Leonis himself neither did nor said anything at that time which gave the slightest indication that he hoped to see his son raised one day to high ecclesiastical office. Donna Bona, on the other hand, openly cherished this hope for her stepson, for her husband's Jewish origin was the subject of secret derision in her own circle. She therefore greedily clutched at every device calculated to banish the memory of that fact, and to raise her husband's power and personal prestige in the eyes of the world. (For it was on account of these that she had married him.)

THE chronicle relates:

Petrus Leonis was now so mighty a captain that his like had not been seen in the City of Rome since the days of the Tusculan domination. But this must not be understood in the sense in which it used to be said of that cursed brood. For Petrus Leonis would never have dreamt, like the Counts of Tusculum, of encroaching on the sacred spheres of the Church, but he continued to conduct the great business affairs of his house with the same quiet energy as before his baptism, as if, indeed, the thought had never even entered his head that he was now a Knight and no longer a merchant. When the horses were being saddled among the Crescenti and they were manning the battlements in the fortress of Saint Eustachius, when the Normans summoned their followers and the Bericisi sounded their trumpets, all was quiet in the castle of the Pierleoni save for the clinking of the golden bezants and the light rustling of the strips of parchment on which their number and weight were entered. The Roman captains used to say in derision that, when the Holy See fell vacant, the "Chiesa Pierleoni" (by which they meant the big tower in the Marcellus theater) was the church of the city in which the descent of the Holy Spirit was most fervently prayed for. In truth, if Petrus Leonis then opened his mouth, it was merely to announce in cool, firm tones that his duty was to keep it shut before the wisdom and enlightenment of Holy Church, and this was the first time such a speech had ever been heard from a Roman captain; all the others had always clamored only for a Pope who would be favorable to themselves.

But Johannes Frangipane, when he heard talk of the "Chiesa Pierleoni," carried his head high, for it was no longer behind the scenes, as formerly, but in open triumph that he now associated himself with the fortunes of Petrus Leonis.

Johannes Frangipane to those who talked of the "Chiesa Pierleoni": "Yes, we can now all pray undisturbed." (By which he meant: "Now not one of you dare move a finger against the pair of us.")

"He has the exaggerated zeal of the neophyte," said the captains, of Petrus Leonis, in secret rage. The people, however, said in amazement: "He has the piety of the true convert." But there were some also who said: "He has the cunning of his old Jewish descent, and you will see that with it he will go further than all our captains with their swords." Holy Church herself, however, said neither the one nor the other, but continued quietly to test the baptized Petrus Leonis, as she had tested the unbaptized, and when she had anything to negotiate with the captains of the City, she did not discuss matters with him, but with Johannes Frangipane (she knew, nevertheless, that in reality she was negotiating with Petrus Leonis). But the friendship of Frangipane with the latter endured for exactly the same length of time as this period of probation lasted.

From the archives of our city of Rome, which is called "the Golden." (This name will still be borne by the very last of her stones.)

At that time, from the Porta Asinaria to the church of St. Clement and from the Porta Sassia to the Moles Hadriani, one could still see practically nothing save the havoc and desolation wrought in our streets by the great conflagration of the Normans, when they set fire to the city during their conflicts with the Salian. Thus the Holy Father could not dwell in his own palaces (these stood as if enwalled behind an entrenchment of ruins) but took up his abode on the isle of Lycaonia, at the house of Gratianus Frangipane (he was the nephew of Johannes) whose two towers rise up like the masts of a ship from the river Tiber, in which this island lies as though anchored. Johannes Frangipane said that he had put the Holy Father under the protection of his nephew; but in reality, he had conducted him there not on account of the two small towers of Gratianus, but on account of the three great ones of Petrus Leonis, which stand close to the isle Lycaonia and thus serve to cover it. Truth to tell, Johannes Frangipane did not regard his own house at Sancta Maria Nova as a safe refuge for the Holy Father at that time, for he was erecting there, precisely with the money of his friend Petrus Leonis, those mighty fortifications, which today, as everyone knows, stretch like the claws of a huge stone spider, as far as the Coliseum and the Palace Septemsolia, so that no enemy that rides across the forum can escape them. For the purposes of that construction, it had been first necessary to pull down all the walls, so that while the work was in progress the house of Johannes Frangipane lay open; but ever since the previous troubles, our city had been infested by dangerous gangs of ruffians on account of the infamous heresiarch Guibert, whom the Salian had bequeathed to us, and after whom our good people of Rome have designated that time as the time of "the little Schism or pseudo-Schism," or also as the time of "the precursive Schism." By which we meant that that little Schism preceded the great or real Schism in the manner of a prophecy, just as the eddying flight of the storm-birds merely serves to announce the foam of the raging sea, although in fact resembling it. For just as the Salian Henry IV was never the real Emperor (since he did not receive his crown from the hands of the true Pope), no more, was the schism fomented by Guibert of Ravenna a real schism; it was but the blasphemous game of an impious prince and an apostate bishop. Indeed, the great Schism of the West will not issue from the hands of a king or an emperor, or from those of any other power of this world, but it will issue from the spirit, that is to say, from that of Antichrist. Him, however, we do not expect to come out of Germany, where the emperor comes from, but it is said that he is to be born in the same place as the one who vanquishes him. For this reason, we believe that he is destined to be born in Rome, because it is there that Christ has his throne upon earth.

All this has been told to us by the woman Susa, whom we call the Saint of Sancta Maria de Inferno.

DURING the time of the Little or Precursive Schism.

The chronicle relates:

At that time Johannes Frangipane used to go about among the captains of the City (some of these would willingly have taken sides with Guibert of Ravenna), throwing his sword with one hand, and the purse of his friend Petrus Leonis with the other, on the table of each house. No one could now venture to suggest buying Frangipane, but neither could anyone hope any longer that Frangipane might, as formerly, desert the Holy Father without being bought, and merely from the fickleness of his own nature. For no matter how Frangipane might swagger about and act the prince with his friend's purse, he was nevertheless in reality the helpless prisoner of that purse; indeed he was attached to it as by a chain, and resembled a mastiff, whose bark is by so much the louder the more it feels the pull. Everyone in Rome perceived this quite clearly, some with amusement and some with fury. Only Frangipane himself failed to perceive it; he really believed that he was magnanimously guiding and confirming the first uncertain steps of a neophyte.

JOHANNES Frangipane and Petrus Leonis.

The chronicle relates:

When Johannes Frangipane visited his friend Petrus Leonis, he used to like taking in his arms the latter's two little sons Obicione and Guido, one of whom he had held at the baptismal font. (They clung to the giant, lost in him like little black flies.) But even more than Obicione and Guido, Frangipane liked having in his arms their little sister Tullia. This child was clothed like a Byzantine princess, in a dress that seemed to be made of glass it was so stiff, and the hem of which was adorned with little gold and silver bells. When Frangipane lifted up the tiny Tullia, the bells began to tinkle like the wedding bells in a children's game. Frangipane's heart would then leap for joy, for he had formed the plan of one day marrying this child to his own son. But of all the children in the house, it was Miriam's little son whom Frangipane loved most to take in his arms. In fact Tullia was almost as puny and pale as Obicione and Guido; and of these two, the robust Frangipane never believed in his heart that they would ever reach manhood. But of the little Petrus he had no such doubt, for he was strong and beautiful like his mother Miriam, and that pleased Frangipane. He never missed an opportunity of asking whether they were not going to take off his little red coat and give him back to the world. But it did not often happen that Frangipane could put this question and take the child in his arms, for the little Petrus always ran away as soon as he heard his step or his voice. (Later they used to say that the child had learnt from the old Rachel that it was the arms of Frangipane that had carried him off from the Jewish quarter.)

The old Rachel and the child Petrus.

We have never been able to find out exactly what the old Rachel related to the little Petrus, but we only know this: Rachel used to chant him a song which is included among the Psalms of the Bible, but which the Christians are loath to sing. It begins:

"The Lord is the God to whom revenge belongeth:
The God of revenge has acted freely.
Lift up thyself, thou that judgest the earth:
Render a reward to the proud!"

One day when the small son of Petrus Leonis was lisping this song with his happy child's voice—the while he shouted for joy and struck the silver table in front of him with his little clenched fists—one of the palace servants laughingly asked him on whom he was calling down such terrible vengeance.

The child with the innocent air of a little bird that has been taught to prattle: "On all the betrayers of our people Israel."

Whereupon the man called some of the other servants of the palace, and repeated his question to the boy. In this way they amused themselves for quite a while with his answer.

THE little Petrus Pier Leonis and the servants of the palace.

The servants: "Which of us do you love most, little master?"

The child: "I love Rachel most."

They: "But you are so smart, little master, and Rachel is such an awful sight. Aren't you afraid of her big, hooked nose?"

The child: "Rachel is not an awful sight, and her nose is very beautiful. It is you who are ugly."

Whereupon the servants continued to amuse themselves at his expense.

THE servants of the palace and the little Petrus Pier Leonis.

At a certain hour every day the servants issued from the palace gate carrying baskets in their hands, out of which they handed bread to the children of Petrus Leonis, which these distributed among the children of the poor who waited outside the gate. But there were always several children also—such as had managed to slip away from their parents—from the Jewish quarter among them, for there are many poor people there just as among the Christians.

When it was the turn of the little Petrus to distribute the bread, he always gave it first to the Jewish children.

One of the palace servants to his comrades: "Our little master picks his own kind out of the crowd, just as one draws fish with a net out of the water; it is as if his little hand attracted them to it from a distance, without his knowing it. This strikes me as very remarkable, as his father will no longer own to his own blood."

Another, reflecting: "Our little master pleases me better than our big master!"

But Donna Bona, who happened to be present one day when the little Petrus was favoring the Jewish children in this manner, gave orders that in the future her husband's children were to remain in the palace when bread was distributed.

DONNA Bona and her husband's children.

Donna Bona did not allow her husband's children to play about in the public place before the castle, or on the neighboring Tiber bank, for she was afraid of the children of her brothers, the Bericisi, who used to play their rough-and-tumble games there. These big, blond, unruly youngsters would sometimes run up to the walls of the Pier Leone castle and make fun of their little swart cousins who stood watching their games with envious eyes from the balcony overlooking the Jewish quarter. (In this they were following the example of their parents at home.)

Once when they were amusing themselves in this way in front of the castle, the voice of Miriam raised in song floated over to them from the white bank in the distance.

The little Petrus Pier Leonis leaning over the balcony: "Who is the woman who sings so beautifully?"

The little Bericisi: "It is one of your grandmothers." (By which they meant: it is a woman of the Ghetto, like you.) But immediately afterwards they made off as fast as their legs could carry them, for on the balcony they had espied the dignified form of Petrus Leonis seated there in oriental majesty. They need not have run away, however, for Petrus Leonis never showed it, when he heard sneers of this kind, but it was as if they did not concern him, and he really had, as the palace servants said, completely forgotten his origin.

THE chronicle relates:

At that time our Holy Father Urban II, who then occupied the See of St. Peter, made his voice the voice of the Holy Sepulcher at Jerusalem, in order that he might inflame Christendom against the East, and redeem a Christian chivalry from the curse of wars made for temporal gain. (For he who takes the Cross wins with his sword, not the earthly, but the heavenly city.) But the Devil, as is his wont, sowed tares among the seeds of the Holy Father, and fooled those who were willing to listen to him, by preaching to them a Crusade of his own. There journeyed through the lands in those days not only the messengers from Rome, preaching to the peoples that they must make ready to sacrifice this temporal life in order to win life eternal, but those also of the great Venetian and Genoese merchants, in their silk and brocaded mantles which are impregnated with all the perfumes of Schiraz and Arabia. But these did not preach the city of eternal glory, but they preached the palaces of the caliphs and the costly carpets of the golden mosques and the great treasure of the Temple of Jerusalem, which Count Tancred was later to plunder.

The Venetians and Genoese, unfolding their glittering mantles, so that the mixture of perfumes might go to the heads of their hearers: "See, this splendor awaits each one of you who registers his name with us for the passage to the Holy Land."

For the Venetians and Genoese, who hoped to embark the Crusaders on their ships, certainly raised anchor in the name of the Holy Trinity, but they did so only after they had contrived to squeeze almost the last brass farthing out of everyone on board.

But when our Holy Father Urban II learned that these people were seeking to make a business out of his holy will and that of Christendom, his anger and grief knew no bounds, and he cried out: "Can it really be then, as Our Savior said, that it is easier for a camel to pass through the eye of a needle than for a rich man to enter into the kingdom of heaven?"

Hereupon one of the Cardinals reminded him of Petrus Leonis, whose wealth surpassed that of all the Venetian and Genoese merchants, and of whom it was known that he had given back his father's usurious gains even before his baptism. But he added that it would be a great and worthy testimony to the sincerity of the onetime Jew's conversion, and at the same time his noblest reward, if he were allowed to serve the great Christian host which was leaving for Jerusalem.

Accordingly the Holy Father sent for Petrus Leonis.

But Johannes Frangipane, when he heard of this, said: "Why did not the Holy Father send for me? I could have transmitted his instructions to Petrus Leonis very effectively."

FROM the archives of our City, which is called "Rome, the Golden."

In those days we saw for the first time one of our captains (namely Petrus Leonis) decorated with the noble sign of those who are willing to go and fight for Christ's Sepulcher and Kingdom in the Holy Land. For it was with our city then, just as it had been when it was a question of our taking part in the struggle against the simoniacs: the whole of Christendom rose at the call of the Holy Father, only the city of the Holy Father himself remained deaf to it.

This was the song which the pilgrims from France and Germany used to sing in our streets at that time:

> "In God's Name we set out,
> His Grace beseech we,
> So help us the arm of God and the Holy Sepulcher
> Wherein lay God himself:
> Kyrie eleison!"

But those who chanted it told us that in the far-off lands beyond the Alps, though it was the season of brown-leafed autumn, the country was white with blossoming trees along all the roads by which the streams of pilgrims passed, as if even blind nature had risen from the grave in order to attest God's grace to his Christian children. We, however, did not believe this, for among us at Rome, there was no white to be seen save the whiteness of the wild, ancient marble, wherein our hard-bitten captains have perched their nests.

The Roman captains among themselves: "Our City is holy like the City of Jerusalem; so let the pilgrims come to us! Why should they bear their costly offerings to orient lands?" But to the pilgrims themselves they said: "You wish to conquer the Tomb of Christ, but in sooth it will be your own tomb. Remain here!"

The pilgrims: "If only it might be as you say! Would that we might die on this journey, that we may rise again among the Blessed!"

PETRUS Leonis decorated with the Cross:

He had asked the Holy Father for permission to wear it, for it was his intention, he said, to join the pilgrims himself, and to depart for the Holy Land in one of the vessels he had bought from the Venetians and Genoese.

THE chronicle relates:

Petrus Leonis was not a man of handsome face or fine stature, but his appearance was none the less very impressive, as of a man who knows that he conducts his affairs in an able and upright manner. He wore with becoming dignity the knight's sword at his side, the tall mitre of the senators on his head (both slightly too large for his figure), and the red cross on his shoulder; this last looked like a little rose which had been plucked from one of our bushes and been somehow grafted on to an exotic date-palm.

Johannes Frangipane to the captains (for he was furious when Petrus Leonis took the cross, as if, in doing so, the latter had done him an ill turn with the Holy Father): "This fellow at any rate will return safe and sound, for out there in the East, Saracens and Jews hold loyally together, and they will all regard him as one of themselves. If anything happens to him, it will only be because he has had the bad luck to fall in with those who have been storming Jerusalem on the banks of the Rhine." (Frangipane was here referring to the wild bands of Crusaders who had gone on ahead of the main body of the holy army, and indulging in every sort of license, had butchered many Jews at Worms and Speyer, thereby striking a cruel blow at the heart of our Holy Father's intention in preaching the Crusade.)

THE Intention of the Holy Father.

As related by the woman Susa, whom we call the Saint of Sancta Maria de Inferno: "Every night I hear our Holy Father pray in his heart, as I heard him pray when he stood on the great plain of Clarus Mons [Clermont] where thousands upon thousands took the cross in response to his sermon. But then no one understood the prayer of our Holy Father, so loud was the rustling of the coats of mail at his feet, for as far as the heavens reached, naught could be seen but kneeling knights whose fierce ardor made tumult under their coats of mail, so that it was as if an iron sea were rolling against the Holy Father's prayer."

THE Prayer of the Holy Father.

As related by the woman Susa: "When our Holy Father Urban recited the great Litany of the Saints on the plain of Clarus Mons and came to the passage where it says: 'That thou wouldst vouchsafe to humble the enemies of Holy Church; we beseech thee, hear us!' he turned his face towards the East, and continued:

"'That thou wouldst vouchsafe to grant a victorious sword to thy Christian Knights in the East; we beseech thee, hear us!

"'That thou wouldst vouchsafe to grant a merciful sword to thy Christian Knights in the East; we beseech thee, hear us!

"'That thou wouldst vouchsafe to grant to the Christian Knights in the East the grace of bringing the souls of all infidels to Baptism; we beseech thee, hear us!'"

THE chronicle relates:

At that time they noticed in the palace of Petrus Leonis that Miriam's little son had become more frightened than ever when he heard the footsteps of Frangipane. Sometimes he ran from room to room, so that Donna Bona in her long silk robes had difficulty in following him, or he hid himself for hours crouched at the bottom of a dark corridor. Donna Bona thought he was playing a prank on her; but when she dragged him out of his hiding-place, the face that looked up at her out of the little red coat was as pale as the head of a white poppy in a field of purple flowers. They told the child that his father's towers were the highest and strongest in the whole city, so that the Holy Father himself felt more protected under their shadow than in any other place; but it almost seemed as if this terrified the boy still more, or as if his fear resided in a part of his consciousness to which no one had access.

THE chronicle relates:

One day a maid in Petrus Leonis's house went to Donna Bona and informed her that for some time past she had frequently observed a dark bearded man steal into the palace courtyard at nightfall and hold long conversations with the old Rachel and the little boy Petrus. Once she had concealed herself and listened to their talk; he spoke of the river Rhine, whose waters were red and gurgling with the blood of the German Jews whom the Crusaders had put to the sword. She was of the opinion that this was the cause of the child's terror, for she had heard him sobbing bitterly during the stranger's narrative.

At this, Donna Bona turned pale: "But the boy isn't a Jew!" Then suddenly, as if someone had thrown a handful of roseleaves in her face: "Just remember that!" And so saying she struck the maid a resounding blow on her cheek. But when this happened, our Holy Father Urban II had already taken up his abode in the house of Petrus Leonis.

THE Holy Father Urban II and Petrus Leonis.

This Pope, who had preached the cross, also died under the cross, that is to say, as a fugitive like the Holy Father Gregory VII, whose example he had zealously followed in all things.

When Johannes Frangipane learned that the Holy Father was in constant communication with Petrus Leonis regarding the transport of the pilgrims to the East, he secretly approached the other captains of the City and gave them to understand that he would raise no opposition if they brought Guibert of Ravenna back to Rome for a while; for his plan was to drive him out again later, and thereby win the Holy

Father's gratitude and push Petrus Leonis into the background once more. Accordingly the captains went and fetched the heresiarch from his place of refuge on the Tiber, and promptly installed him at St. Peter's.

When the noise of the tumult reached the isle of Lycaonia, Petrus Leonis opened the gates of his mansion, which stood nearby, and going forth with a numerous escort, respectfully begged the Holy Father to take up his abode with him until the revolt had been subdued. The Holy Father accepted the offer and accompanied him back.

This, they say, was the first great victory of Petrus Leonis over Johannes Frangipane.

Our Holy Father Urban II in the house of Petrus Leonis.

Petrus Leonis had a room in his house wherein was a rich couch as sumptuous as the bed of King Solomon, of which the Canticle speaks: it was supported by columns, and furnished with purple cushions, and the wooden frame was mounted with gold and ivory like the Ark of the Covenant. Since Petrus Leonis's marriage with Miriam, no one had dared to lie in it.

When the Holy Father took up his abode with Petrus Leonis, the latter led him to this bed, as being the place of honor in his house, and requested him to use it as his resting-place. But God had ordained that in this bed the Holy Father should rest for ever from all the sorrows and tribulations of his mortal life.

On learning that the Holy Father had taken refuge in the house of Petrus Leonis, Johannes Frangipane rose like a furious storm, and again drove the heresiarch from the city, thinking that he would now be able to bring back his friend's illustrious guest in triumph to the isle of Lycaonia. But he was told that the Holy Father was stricken down with grief, and that he was unable to leave his bed (for the Holy Father well knew who was at the back of the impious revolt).

Johannes Frangipane bursting in on the Holy Father, with smoking sword: "Holy Father, the way is free. I have driven your adversary out of the city."

The Holy Father: "And where are the souls of those whom, in doing so, your sword must have slaughtered without need?"

Frangipane (with uncontrolled passion): "They are only the souls of vile Guibertists, and of no more account than the souls of the infidel Saracens whom the holy army is now slaying in the East."

The Holy Father: "Johannes Frangipane, did you not pray with me in the great Litany for a merciful sword?"

At this Frangipane was silent, for he did not know what the Holy Father meant. Later, when he had left the house of Petrus Leonis, he said to his nephew Gratianus: "I do not think the Holy Father will last much longer, for he is already delirious!"

THE death of Pope Urban II.

The chronicle relates:

When the last hour of the Holy Father Urban II drew near, Petrus Leonis asked him to bless himself and his family but especially his little son Petrus whom he had destined for the service of Holy Church; and to this the Holy Father readily consented.

The child was sent for: he entered, led by the blonde hand of Donna Bona in all her silks, deathly pale under his black hair; and when they signed to him to kneel down, it was as if little supports snapped and gave way under him. As he lay on the ground in his little red coat he looked very helpless and forlorn, like a flower-bud that has been torn from the earth.

The windows were wide open: the hot, blue summer air came in, mingled with the murmurs of people at prayer (for the whole palace staff were on their knees in the court below, and up the length of the staircase, owing to the approaching death of the illustrious guest).

Meanwhile the Holy Father had been raised on his pillows. But as he was lifting his trembling old man's hand above the boy's head, in order to bless him, suddenly the clatter of a horse's hoof at full gallop was heard in the street, followed immediately by the cry: "Allelujah! Allelujah!" The cry rushed up past the crowd of kneeling figures on the stairs and beat like palm-branches against the door of the room. At once Petrus Leonis went out to inquire what it meant.

A Norman knight, covered with sweat, on his knees before the door, exhausted and breathless: "Holy Father, do not die before you have heard my news! The city of Jerusalem has fallen; three thousand Saracens have been put to the sword, and seven hundred Jews have been burned in their own Synagogue! Not a single enemy of Christ has escaped the sword of the holy army!"

All those in the room now also shouted "Allelujah." Only the Holy Father did not cry "Allelujah," but he looked at Petrus Leonis.

Suddenly a voice (it was that of Frangipane): "It is not the Holy Father, it is Petrus Leonis who is dying!"

At these words Petrus Leonis, once again, with hollow voice, pale as death, echoed alone: "Allelujah!" (But the child's cry of horror as he made his escape seemed to cut the word in two.) At the same moment the Holy Father sank back and passed away with a sudden seizure.

They say in Rome that it was his joy at learning of the fall of Jerusalem that killed him.

THE chronicle relates:

A short while later, the report spread in the palace of Petrus Leonis that the old Rachel had somehow contrived to have the little Petrus secretly circumcised, and that this accounted for his terror of the Christians. But when Rachel was questioned on the point, she merely shook her head, as if she did not understand what the palace gossips were talking about.

The palace servants among themselves: "She is not so stupid as she likes to pretend, and if our master put her the plain question himself he could easily make her confess."

But Petrus Leonis, when the rumor reached his ears, did not send for Rachel and question her, but kept silent, and gave his son to the fathers of Saint Alexius to bring up. After this, the rumor died down. But of the fathers of Saint Alexius it is said that they received the timid child with the charming greeting: "Welcome, little son of the great Prophets and Apostles."

It came to our knowledge, however, that at first the good fathers found the little Petrus Pier Leonis exceedingly difficult to handle. The child was so timid that he even hid himself from his own father, when the latter came to the monastery to see him.

The fathers of Saint Alexius among themselves: "We know that Petrus Leonis is a man who never acts harshly or unjustly even in his dealings with his servants, still less would he so act towards his own dear son. And yet the boy seems more terrified of his father than of anybody."

They then tried to make excuses to Petrus Leonis for not being able to find the child at that moment. But Petrus Leonis did not give them time to explain; his usual sedateness suddenly left him, and he departed in a violent hurry, as if he had no wish to hear anything. At this the good fathers were even more bewildered than they had been at the behavior of the boy.

III

---◆---

THE Well of Saint Johannes in Fonte whence they draw the baptismal water: The upper part is decorated with new white marble. The molding is supported by small columns, all twisted and inlaid with little stone fillets of red, black and gold, in the manner of the Cosmati. But in the interior, where the spring gushes forth in its depths, the sides are masonried with an ancient melancholy-looking stone. When the sun rests on the edge like a large, white peacock in the midday light, there is sometimes a gurgling and tossing about at the bottom, as if the spring were trying to force its way out. But no one pays any attention.

THE Jews of Rome relate:

This year, when the community kept the 9 Av. (that is the day on which in the long ago the holy Temple was twice destroyed, the first time by King Nebuchadnezzar, and later by Titus, the Roman), the bells of the city were still ringing their joy-peals over the capture of Jerusalem by the Christians, and all the people were shouting themselves hoarse in laudation of the glorious death of Pope Urban.

Amid all this noise of bells and jubilation, the Jews had gathered together in their Synagogue (today this was almost in complete darkness, for on the 9 Av. only a single candle may burn), when it happened, while they were intoning the Lamentations of the Prophet Jeremiah, that the light rocking motion of the men on their knees suddenly became quicker

and more violent than is usual among Jews at their prayers. At first, each
thought it was happening to himself alone (for in the darkness no one
could distinguish his neighbor); but soon, it was as though an uncontrol-
lable anguish bursting from every corner of the room had seized hold of
all of them, sweeping their knees from under them, and causing them to
strike their breasts and heads against the walls and chairs—those who
had nothing in front of them fell heavily to the ground. The women,
who sat crouching behind the balustrade above, hearing the heartrending motions and lamentations of their men in the darkness below, began
weeping and sobbing in sympathy and terror. Only the Rabbi Nathan
ben Jechiel did not make violent motions with his head, but we could see
him kneeling before the holy Ark in the light of the single candle, with
head stiff and erect as this last, while his voice rose clear and calm above
the weepings and groanings of the others:

> "Why has a living man murmured, man suffering for his sins?
> Let us search our ways, and seek and return to the Lord.
> Let us lift up our hearts, with our hands to the Lord in the heavens.
> We have done wickedly and provoked Thee to wrath; therefore
>   Thou art inexorable.
> Thou hast covered in Thy wrath and hast struck us:
> Thou hast killed and hast not spared."

Meanwhile the physical commotion behind the Rabbi became
wilder and wilder; more and more frenzied rose the wailing in the darkness, and more and more despairing grew the weeping and sobbing of
the women. And gradually the voice of the Rabbi ceased to be heard; it
was swallowed up by another voice, which was at first as if someone were
darting about, crying here and there in the darkness, and then suddenly
as if he shouted with a hundred throats at once:

"Jerusalem has been destroyed for the third time! Jerusalem has been
destroyed for the third time!"

Indeed, the voice cried not with a hundred throats, but it cried with thousands of throats (which, however, were not there), as if here in this small, dark Synagogue in Rome, the sorrow of a whole people were suddenly breaking out, the myriad streams of its sufferings having converged there from all the lands of its dispersion and from all the centuries of its exile. And thus the whole Synagogue was nothing more than a single cry: "Jerusalem! Jerusalem! Jerusalem!" Until at last every voice was still, and only the dark space of the room heaved up and down as with the waves of a flood; for now it was not only the women who wept, but the men also, like helpless children.

Later, when it seemed as though the whole community must be drowned in their tears, a voice was again raised, clear as a star over the sea, crying: "The Messiah is coming."

THE women of the Jews relate:

Next day, while the city was still ringing its bells, a rumor spread among the Romans from mouth to mouth and from church to church: "A light in the Arch of the seven-branched candlestick! All its marble lights were burning during the night! The sound of the sacred Trumpet was also heard! See how the City of Jerusalem rejoices at being in the hands of the Christians!" (Now there exists a prophecy among us that when the Messiah comes, the seven-branched candlestick in the Arch of Titus will begin to burn, and the call of the sacred Trumpet will resound therein. But during the Crusade the Goyim said that if these two things happened it would mean that Jerusalem had fallen.)

The following night—our men were all in bed, recovering from the injuries they had inflicted upon themselves—Esther, the wife of Mosche ben Salomo, and Judith, the daughter of Josua ben Nachmann, crept secretly through the valley of the Cerchi along the wall of our cemetery and up the Palatine Hill; from there across the forest of ruins, over the marble roots and rubble down to the Arch of the seven-branched candlestick (they could not pass through it; none of our folk will do this, for the Arch was erected in triumph over Israel's fall). In the grey of early morning they returned with torn shoes and bedraggled hair, and announced:

"Yes, the candlestick is really burning! We saw the shine of little red flames issuing from the hollow of the Arch, and at dawn, when the horns of our captains were silent, we heard on our way home the sacred Trumpet." This was the news that Esther and Judith brought to our sick men.

Now, when the Rabbi Nathan ben Jechiel came to hear of it, fearing that a tumult might arise, he invited the older women of the community to his house, and asked which of us had raised the cry: "The Messiah is coming!" in the Synagogue. We replied that we could not possibly say, for our ears had been filled with sobbings, but that the voice had sounded very mysterious and strangely resonant like the voice of an angel.

The Rabbi Nathan ben Jechiel (he is surnamed the "Stern" and so he looked at that moment): "But it was not the voice of an angel: it was the voice of a woman."

Whereupon Esther, the wife of Mosche ben Salomo, who had gone to the Arch of the seven-branched candlestick: "But could not an angel have made use of a woman's voice?"

The Rabbi Nathan ben Jechiel: "No, that is not possible, for the angels know that a woman may not raise her voice in the Synagogue."

He then questioned us again, but was unable to extract from us the information he wanted, for some of us really believed that an angel had been present in the Synagogue, but most of us did not wish to betray Miriam.

MIRIAM and the cry.

The women of the Jews relate:

We were still in the days when practically only women were to be seen in our streets, for our men had not yet recovered from their fever, and lay in bed with their bruised heads swathed in towels, and many of them suffering acute pain. It is well, we said, that the Romans are still hanging on to their bells, and give no heed to us; otherwise they might suspect that a secret plot was brewing in our midst, or, if they found out the truth, they might begin jeering at us (for there is no pity in their hearts for our poor disinherited race).

In the evenings, however, when, over the city and its wide, deserted squares, the heat of the day had settled in a fiery glow as of vast, white funeral pyres (these glowing heaps having been built up, as it were, out of the debris of ancient marble, which lies everywhere about) and we women sat before our doors, straining our ears, and wondering whether we should hear the call of the sacred Trumpet in the distant night, or bemoaning to each other the unhappy lot of our men—then Miriam bade Esther and Judith mount the small belvedere of Gerschom ben Joel (one can hear further from there than down in the narrow street), while she herself gathered her sorrowing sisters around her and tried to soothe them.

MIRIAM consoling us:

"Hear me, dear sisters! Dear sisters, look at me! Here you see a mother without the crown of her life: a mother without her son. Here stands one who has been in the night of death, nay who was herself the night of death for her own babe. But the Lord gave life to my death with a great promise, he opened the coffin of my dead flesh to a living daughter: and she shall bring back to me the crown of my life. And so too will Israel pass through the death-night of her sorrow! For our God is the God of great miracles. Come, say with me, all of you: 'The Lord will fulfill the promises of Israel!'"

Many of us then said after her: "Yes, the Lord will fulfill the promises of Israel!" But others also replied: "We no longer know the promises you mean; it is a long time since they were given to us. Maybe they are already dead. And as for your son, Miriam, so far we have never even seen him."

At this Miriam said: "Very well, I will prove to you that the promises of the Lord are living!"

She then went into the house, took her child from the cot where she was sleeping, brought her out and placed her in the middle of our circle.

Miriam: "Behold my living promise! It is she who shall announce to you the promise of Israel!" She then told her child to recite the great canticles and words of our Prophets, with which from her earliest years she had sung her to sleep.

MIRIAM's child:

She stood on a slight rise in the ground; opposite on the wall of the house hung a lamp, whose light from out its niche drew a golden ray round her blind face. She was still warm and flushed from the sweet intoxication of her slumbers, and at first her sleepy voice stumbled a little over the words; but she struggled on with docile obedience, and soon spoke the great words out with the charming vivacity that children bring to the recital of their little verses.

THE child:

"Arise, be enlightened, O Jerusalem:
for thy light is come,
and the glory of the Lord is risen upon thee!
For behold, darkness shall cover the earth and a mist the people;
but the Lord shall arise upon thee
and his glory shall be seen upon thee!"

Many of our women, who had previously murmured, now wept for tenderness and shame, and said: "Verily, He who has thus let his praises be spoken by the mouth of an innocent child, will also be able to fulfill Israel's promise."

Only Lea, the widow of Benjamin ben Jacob, and Paula, the wife of Leon ben Samuel, did not say: "The Lord will fulfill Israel's promise"; for Lea had two sons on a pilgrimage to Jerusalem, and she believed them to have fallen there, and Paula's husband was the most seriously ill of all our men.

Then Miriam took the little Trophäea by the hand, and led her to Lea, the widow of Benjamin ben Jacob, and bade her speak to her these words:

"A child is born to us
And a son is given to us,
and the government is upon his shoulder:
And his name shall be called
Wonderful Counsellor, God the Mighty,
Father of the world to come, the Prince of Peace!"

Then she led the child to Paula, the wife of Leon ben Samuel, and bade her say:

"He will seek that which was lost,
and that which was driven away he will bring again;
and he will bind up that which was broken,
and he will strengthen that which was weak,
and he will preserve them, and feed them in judgment."

And now Lea and Paula also said, albeit through their tears: "Yes, the Lord will fulfill the promises of Israel, the Messiah will come." (But the whole time the child was speaking, one heard far and near the incessant blowing of horns from the towers of our captains.)

In the meantime, Hannah Naemi, who was standing in the shadow of the door-post, became anxious about Miriam. For Hannah Naemi was old, and she heard in her blood the voices of many who were yet older than she, and it seemed to her that she had already lived through all this many times before.

Hannah Naemi in the shadow of the door-post: "Miriam, if the Messiah comes, I will tear branches from the trees and the clothes from my body, to spread them beneath his feet, and I will cry out: 'Praise be to him, who comes in the name of the Lord!' But now it is time your poor little child was put to sleep."

Miriam in reply: "Go to sleep yourself, Hannah Naemi!"

At that moment a sharp clear sound rang out, piercing like a star the blunt horn-tones of the captains.

Esther and Judith on the belvedere of Gerschom ben Joel, jumping up with a bound: "The sacred Trumpet! The sacred Trumpet!"

Then all took up the cry, almost sobbing with fear in their excess of joy: "The sacred Trumpet!"

When Hannah Naemi heard this, she said: "Before I go to sleep, you would do well to wake up!" She then went into the house to her brother.

HANNAH Naemi and her brother.

He sat buried in the holy scriptures, his head surrounded by his mass of white hair, as by a halo of grave thoughts.

Hannah Naemi (hesitatingly, for she loved him dearly): "My friend, have our masters taught anything about the time when we ought to believe that the Messiah will come?"

The Rabbi Nathan ben Jechiel (taken aback, for Hannah Naemi was humble and never troubled herself about the wisdom of the schools, which is the province of the men; then kindly, for he was a just man): "Yes, Hannah Naemi, our masters teach us a doctrine in regard thereto, and it is this: 'A thousand years in the sight of the Lord are as yesterday which is past, or as a watch in the night.'"

Hannah Naemi: "And if someone should say: 'The thousand years are passed, and the watch in the night also will come to an end'?"

The Rabbi Nathan ben Jechiel (his brow quivered, his eyes shot flame, but his tone was cold and firm): "To him shall one reply: 'So speaks the God of Israel, the Eternal and Omniscient, who permits not that one question him, and whom one does not question: For my thoughts are not your thoughts, nor your ways my ways.'"

Hannah Naemi: "Very well then, tell this to your daughter Miriam."

Then the Rabbi knew that it was Miriam who had cried out in the Synagogue: "The Messiah is coming!"

The Rabbi Nathan ben Jechiel (for he respected the great martyrdom of his daughter at the birth of her child): "She is the only one among all the women of our community whom I cannot reprove, but may the Lord have mercy on her!"

THE Women of the Jews relate:

Meanwhile we had all sprung up from our seats, and credulous and incredulous, young and old, hale and infirm, we all of us rushed out of the narrow streets towards the White Bank, in the direction of the sound (for there was none of us who had not heard it).

The bank was lonely and deserted; a wind was blowing there from over the river, bearing under its wings all manner of sounds such as rise by night in the cities of men: bells and horns, groans and cries, singing and laughter, rushing water, owls and frogs all crushed together under the wings of this somber wind, and scattered like so much dust.

While we thus stood on the bank with beating hearts and ears strained, searching, as it were, this medley of sounds for the one that was ours, Miriam told her child to speak once again:

> "Rejoice with Jerusalem, and be glad with her,
> all you that love her!
> Rejoice for joy with her,
> all you that mourn for her!
> You shall exult and be filled
> with the abundance of your consolations!"

At that moment the sharp, clear note again flashed through the night like a star, but this time quite near, as if a silver arrow whizzed towards us.

Already there was the noise of galloping and trumpeting amid the rubble and debris of the bank, together with much shouting and flying of dust: "Make way there, make way, you Jewish women, for the riders of the illustrious captains!" (But there was plenty of room both for us and the riders.) Suddenly the horses stopped with their hoofs raised high over our heads, neighing and rearing as if in fright (for beast does not trample on man; it is only man who tramples on man).

We dispersed with shrieks, like a swarm of birds in the darkness. Only the child in her blindness stood still; then she ran, with her little dress flying about her, into the midst of the trumpets.

Hannah Naemi, carrying the child home (for we had rescued her from beneath the fallen horse of one of the riders): "Alas! Miriam, your little girl has now met her brother's world for the first time!"

Miriam, unmoved: "Yes, she has put herself in the way of the horsemen of Edom, and as a result, one of them has been overthrown."

THE Women of the Jews relate:

From that day we did not gather round Miriam any more, to await the Messiah. Moreover, our men were now up again and had returned to their work. The Rabbi sent some of them to the Arch of the seven-branched candlestick, and they brought back the following account: "The builders of the Frangipani are erecting a high tower above this Arch, and have hung lamps there, lest anyone should come by night and make off with their tools and materials unobserved. But as regards the sacred Trumpet, it was only one of the new silver horns which Petrus Leonis was having tested."

Since that time people have arisen among us, who say: "Why do we waste our time always mourning for Jerusalem? Rome also is a beautiful city, where one can live pleasantly enough. We have dwelt here now for a thousand years and more, let us then love this place, as though it were our own homeland, for after all, it was the Lord who led us hither."

And we others have had nothing to reply to them, for man must have a piece of earth beneath his feet, otherwise his heart dries up within him.

And so we forgot the silver trumpets.

Only the little Trophäea has said from time to time: "My brother passed by then, and did not recognize me, but I can see more clearly than he."

It was this saying of the child which afterwards gave rise to the story that those riders were really the riders of Petrus Leonis, and that they had had with them Miriam's little son, whom they were taking to the monastery of Saint Alexius.

IV

THE monastery of Saint Alexius. It is situated on the Aventine Hill near the Basilica of Sancta Sabina. Among the monasteries of Rome, none is more illustrious than Saint Alexius; there, if anywhere, is the seat of the spirit of Cluny. Many pious monks dwell in this monastery; great bishops, far-famed for the holiness of their lives, have been trained within its walls; eminent theologians and scholars learned in the holy Scriptures likewise flourish there. Among these latter is Father Aegidius; he knows and reads all the writings of the Old Testament in the language of the Hebrews, and interprets them in accordance with the fulfillment of the New.

THE Monastery of Saint Alexius.

The church of the monastery has a tall, light-brown steeple, which climbs tapering to the sky like the steeples of Saint Gregorius in Velabro and Sancta Maria in Schola Greca. From its height the swallows swoop down to the Tiber and caress with their dark wings the silvery waters downstream as far as the Pons Judaeorum. There they disappear for a while under the roofs of the Jews.

When from the garden-wall of the monastery, Father Aegidius allowed the eyes of little Petrus Pier Leonis to become swallows, he always bade them fly in that direction. At the same time he never forgot to say that the Jewish quarter lay down there beside the river, as small and hidden in the great city of Rome as was the basket in the reeds wherein Pharaoh's daughter had one day found the child Moses, and he added that the little Petrus had himself been saved, like an infant Moses, from the fate of all the other poor Jewish children.

He would then take the child across to the church of Sancta Sabina, where there is a massive door made of cypress wood, which is known as the "High Door." This door is carved with many pictures from the history of the Old and New Testaments. On it Father Aegidius would point out to the boy the passage of the children of Israel through the Red Sea, in the course of which the army of King Pharaoh perished so miserably; and then he would pass on to the miracles of the water and the manna and to the great miracle of the Brazen Serpent, all produced in the desert by the power of God working in the child Moses now grown to manhood. In the same way, explained the good Father, the little Petrus was also destined to a great work in the Kingdom of God, namely to the service of Holy Church. Indeed she herself had been the King's daughter, who had saved him from the city of the Jews, just as Pharaoh's daughter had saved the infant Moses.

Once, when Father Aegidius had been talking in this way, the boy replied (his gaze fixed the while on the passage through the Red Sea): "But the child Moses brought disaster to the people of Pharaoh's daughter."

At this the good Father was taken aback, and felt a little alarmed at the sagacity of the boy who had so cruelly destroyed the beautiful symbol he had presented to him. But he was unable to contradict him.

THE young Petrus Pier Leonis.

He now no longer wore a little red silk coat as in his father's palace, but the severe uniform of the monastery pupils; nevertheless his companions continued to call him the "little Cardinal." But they gave him this name owing to his quickness of mind and cleverness of tongue, for they felt with these two gifts he could not fail one day to become a great personage. There were some, however, who gave it to him because they believed that he himself cherished such an ambition; for the boy put his fellow-pupils to shame not only by his gifts, but by the zeal with which he set himself to excel them all in everything. On account of this zeal many of them bore him a secret grudge.

THE young Petrus Pier Leonis.

…he was now no longer timid as formerly, nor was he afraid of his father, but met him with self-assurance, knowing full well that he was the show-boy of the monastery school. Indeed, when his father rode out with princely pomp to visit him at Saint Alexius, the boy made no attempt to conceal his joy and pride; and this aroused still further ill-feeling among his companions.

These latter to the good monks: "He is just as vain of his father's gold and power as he is of his own brains and knowledge."

The good monks: "Why should he not rejoice in the gifts with which God has blessed him and his father? To take pride in gold and intellect is not so bad, in our view, as to envy others on account of them."

The pupils among themselves: "It seems to us that the Fathers of this monastery are themselves all too ready to vaunt their pride in the young Petrus. No wonder he is becoming so mightily pleased with himself!"

THE Fathers of the Monastery and the young Petrus.

One day, when our Holy Father Paschal II (he was the Pope elected after the death of Urban) visited the monastery of Saint Alexius, the good monks arranged for the young Petrus Pier Leonis to receive him with a poem of welcome. With his slim form and brownish complexion, the boy looked like a young David as he stood there reciting his poem—he had composed it himself—in the monastery porch, and the sonorous leonines sprang from his lips with such ease and assurance that one might have thought he was in the habit of conversing in leonines. The Holy Father and all who accompanied him could hardly find words to express their astonishment.

Later, when the Pope inquired about him, the good monks informed him (for they were proud of this product of their educational skill) that the young scholar who had so impressed him was none other than the small shy son of Petrus Leonis, who had once fled shrieking with terror from the death-chamber of Pope Urban. Whereupon the Holy Father sent for the boy.

The Holy Father Paschal (this Pope was tall and of princely bearing, but his countenance was gentle and kind, like that of a woman) playfully to the young Petrus: "So you are our little son who was seen to run away from his father's blessing?"

The boy, with quick tongue and without any embarrassment: "Give me your blessing now, Holy Father!"

The Holy Father then gave him his blessing. And once again the Fathers of Saint Alexius congratulated themselves on the excellent result of their labors; all save one, who later, when the Holy Father had gone, remarked to his Brothers: "There was more truthfulness in this boy's fear at that time, than there is in his assurance today!"

The monk who spoke was Father Gerbert, who is known in the monastery as "Pater Grammaticus." He is the most ascetic of all the Fathers at Saint Alexius (for otherwise how could he dare to busy himself so unceasingly with the perilous writings of the Pagans?), but he is also the most just of them all. Only towards the son of Petrus Leonis was he observed on many occasions to be unjust. Even those pupils who bore a grudge against the latter because of his excessive zeal, said of Pater Grammaticus: "He pecks at the faults of this boy, like a blind hen that goes about pecking at corn-seeds that are not there. And yet he knows that nothing upsets him so much as injustice."

PATER Grammaticus and the young Petrus Pier Leonis.

Just at that time, everyone in Rome was again talking about the Patarini, who, in the cities of Lombardy (although the simoniacs had been overthrown there), still continued to revolt against their captains; for the people there wanted to rid themselves of the rule of the nobility.

With regard to them, the youthful Benedictus Normannus, one of the pupils at Saint Alexius, remarked one day: "If I were a lord in one of those cities, I would have every tenth person among the people hanged, whether he belonged to the Patarini or not."

Whereupon Pier Leone, trembling like a young tree in a storm, not just at the top, but as it were from the roots upwards: "And I would cut off the hands of anyone who slew an innocent man."

The Fathers of the monastery commended the young Petrus for his eagerness to espouse the cause of the innocent, and only chided him for wanting to cut off people's hands (this sort of language is common among the sons of our captains).

But Pater Grammaticus said to him: "You will have to witness many an injustice, before you can be a priest of Christ."

The boy, scowling: "If I were a priest of Christ, like you, Father, I would fight to abolish injustice on earth!"

The Pater: "Only take care not to abolish the Cross as well!"

PATER Grammaticus and the Fathers of Saint Alexius.

Sometimes these grumbled at him, for it angered them to see him forever finding fault with their best pupil.

To Pater Grammaticus: "We know you are of the opinion that Petrus Leonis was not sincere in the matter of his baptism, and that he only came over to the Church in order to win consideration and success in this world. In our view, however, we have no right to form such a judgment, for we cannot see inside a human soul, and therefore we cannot know if you are right or wrong. But even if you be right, no blame attaches to the boy, since he was an infant who knew nothing of what was happening when they carried him to the baptismal font."

Pater Grammaticus: "No, no blame attaches to the boy, but he is sprung from a race to whom the Lord said: 'I will visit the sins of the fathers on the children down to the third and fourth generation.' Do you not see that in this child is being revealed everything that lies hidden in his father?"

The Fathers of Saint Alexius: "We see, above all, that you yourself would resent being put in the wrong, just like that boy."

Pater Grammaticus: "There, my dear Brothers, you are certainly right: it is only too true, of us as of all men, that no one is born with a love for the Cross!"

THE chronicle relates:

In the year when the two young princes Obicione and Guido were carried off by an epidemic, it was the general expectation that Petrus Leonis would take Miriam's son away from the monastery of Saint Alexius, in order that he might represent his family in the world, since he was now the eldest of his brothers. Johannes Frangipane urged him day and night to do this; he even offered to betroth his niece Jacoba to the young Petrus, if he returned to the world. But Petrus Leonis replied: "God forbid that I should rob Holy Church of my first-born, whom I have dedicated to her!" And he would not hear of it, when he was told that he could be released from his promise, since the young Petrus had not yet taken his vows. This attitude came as a great surprise to many; but there were others who concluded (as did Frangipane in his jealousy) that Petrus Leonis had already formed his own plans in regard to his son's future.

This latter was now a boy of sixteen, but as ripe and clear of purpose as an adult. From his father he inherited firmness and clarity of understanding, but his mind was infused with a kindling flame which the former had never possessed (for Petrus Leonis had never at any time been more than a great, though honest, accountant). From his mother he derived his beautiful eyes and robust frame, and also, it was said, his amatory disposition. The Fathers of Saint Alexius knew that women had troubled him from his earliest years; even as a small boy, he could never behold one without pain and embarrassment, when he thought of his priestly vocation. Nevertheless he was even more violently opposed than his father to the idea of returning to the world.

THE chronicle relates:

One day when the young Petrus had accompanied his father to the house of Johannes Frangipane, the latter so arranged it that Pier Leone was left alone in a room with his niece Jacoba (for he still hoped to attain his ends in this way).

Jacoba Frangipane had by no means a beautiful face, but she had exquisite hands and feet. Accordingly—for her uncle had told her to make herself attractive to the young Petrus—she let a ring that she wore play in the sun: its stone hung on her long white finger like a drop of blood, so that the finger itself, although it remained motionless, seemed to be making mysterious signs. She well knew that the rude sons of the other captains would never notice arts of this kind, but she had been told that Pier Leone had an eye even for the less obvious and minor aspects of a woman's charm.

The young Petrus at once noticed the beauty of her hand, and in order to render her the homage due to it in graceful style, he passed a complimentary remark on the beauty of her ring. (She understood quite well that he was really referring to her hand.)

But at that time, thanks to the Crusaders, we had begun to practice the courtesy of the East, where it is customary, if a guest takes a fancy to anything in one's house, immediately to offer it to him as a present. Accordingly Jacoba took the ring from her finger and handed it to the young Pier Leone. At the same time her face reddened, for just as she had understood his previous admiration of the ring as referring to her hand, so did he now understand her present gesture as likewise referring to it.

The young Petrus Pier Leonis (blushing like Jacoba Frangipane, but unperturbed): "Fair damsel, the bishoprics in the Campania have been impoverished ever since the great Norman invasion. Allow me to place your ring in the empty treasury of the Church; if fate wills, I shall one day take it back as an episcopal ring!"

Not long after this, the young Petrus Pier Leonis received Minor Orders. From that day Johannes Frangipane's jealousy of his friend Petrus Leonis was never extinguished.

JOHANNES Frangipane and Petrus Leonis.

Johannes Frangipane's secret jealousy of Petrus Leonis dates from the day when the latter led our Holy Father Urban II into his house, and ends with the day when King Henry V had himself crowned in St. Peter's. For from this hour, King Henry V may indeed bear the title of Roman Emperor, but it is Petrus Leonis who is known among the people as "King of Rome." From then begins Frangipane's open jealousy of the other.

THE chronicle relates:

As yet they had been unable to settle the great conflict regarding the Investiture of Bishops. Latterly this conflict had fallen asleep, so to speak; but it was a disturbed sleep haunted by troubled dreams. Often at night, the Holy Father Paschal heard it groaning, as it were, in his own slumbers, but the City of Rome, full of alarm, heard it rattling the sword.

At that time there came riders from Germany who brought us the following message: "King Henry (for he had died under the ban of the Church) lies unblessed in his stone coffin; this is miserably stowed away in an unconsecrated side-chapel of the Cathedral of Speyer, with stones heaped up anyhow in front of the door, and a plank leaning against them, to prevent children from clambering over unawares. Night and day, many devout men and women of Speyer are timidly praying from afar for the poor soul of King Henry, but not a single Holy Mass has been offered up for it. Let the Holy Father be merciful, and release the dead King from the ban, but let him crown the living one, his son, Emperor, so that peace may be restored in the Kingdom of Christ."

Some of us, who are wont to pray for the poor souls, then went and asked the woman Susa if we ought to pray for King Henry, or whether it would be useless; in which case we would rather go to the help of another soul, whom we could easily bring to Heaven.

The woman Susa: "You ought certainly to pray for the dead King, but much more ought you to pray for the living King!"

We then asked her what we were to understand by this, for we thought that it would be hard to find anyone with graver sins on his soul than the dead King Henry.

She: "I have a little sister in Germany, who will one day be called my great sister: in seven hundred years' time the church bells all along the Rhine will still be ringing for Saint Hildegarde of Bingen; but today she is only a little child in her father's castle. This same child prayed with King Henry, when he lay confined in that castle as the prisoner of his own son, and thereupon the embittered heart of the old king became as tender again as the holy child's own. (One day this will be known as the first miracle of Saint Hildegarde.) Now if our Holy Father releases King Henry from the ban, and permission is given to remove his wretched remains to consecrated ground, then also his soul will enter heaven. There it will be as small as the King upon earth was great and proud, but precisely this will seem to him a state of blessedness, for while yet on earth he repented of all his sins. But he expiated them in this, that his own son rose against his bodily father, just as he himself had once risen against his spiritual father."

And then once again the woman Susa said: "But pray, all of you, for King Henry, the living!"

KING Henry the living.

(We asked the woman Susa about him.)

"The dead King Henry," she told us, "could be disloyal, and you read it in his face; accordingly his countenance retained a certain nobility to the very last; but the living King Henry is so disloyal that his face no longer betrays it. The dead King Henry had narrow eyes, in the corners of which cowered the treachery he was contemplating, as though he himself were ashamed of it. But the living King Henry has round eyes like pools, in the mirror of which his iniquity lies engulfed. The mouth of the dead King Henry could tremble violently with insolence and pain (and it trembled, when he pursued our Holy Father with the sword), but the living King Henry has a mouth like iron, no agitation can make it move.

All his life, the dead King Henry was without happiness or success, but with the living King Henry, everything he undertakes will succeed."

THE chronicle relates:

Our Holy Father Paschal, who was now called upon to renew the Investiture contest with King Henry VI, bore no resemblance to the Holy Father Gregory VII who had fought with King Henry IV, or rather he resembled him only as the soft radiance of the moon resembles the fiery glow of the noonday sun.

And since all the pious souls of Christendom never ceased to offer up prayers, night and day, that Christ would grant His Vicar the happiness of bringing that lamentable conflict to a peaceful end, without prejudice to the liberties of His Holy Church, the Holy Father Paschal was prompted, in the goodness of his heart, to put forward this compromise: The German Bishops were to restore their Imperial fiefs to the Crown; in this way they would make themselves independent of the secular power; at the same time, that power, being likewise made independent of them, would no longer desire to exercise the Investiture in regard to them (for the Crown desired this only on account of the Regalia). If the King recognized this new Papal ordinance, and in agreement therewith solemnly renounced his claim to the Investiture, so that all danger of future offence and confusion might be removed, the Holy Father on his side would be willing to forget the past, he would release the dead King from the ban, and crown the living King, Emperor.

King Henry V (he was well aware, however, that the Bishops would not give up the Regalia): It certainly lay heavy on his conscience to despoil the Church in this way; nevertheless, if the Holy Father so ordered it, he was ready to submit, and he would come to Rome forthwith, to receive the Imperial Crown.

But we all knew what it means when the Salians come to Rome to receive the Imperial Crown.

THE chronicle relates:

At that time we saw a comet appear, blood-red like the head of a fiery horse that leaps through the clouds, trailing the length of heaven with its tail in one long sweep down to the earth; there it continued its course in a second tail, which swept from the river Rhine over the rocky heights of the Alps down to the plain of Lombardy, as if the star were trailing a procession of iron men behind it.

We have never beheld so many iron men as bore down upon Italy with King Henry, when he came to receive the crown.

FROM the archives of our golden city of Rome:

Later one often heard the question discussed among us: Why did we allow the King to enter our city? It was clear that he came as an oppressor; the Lombards, through whose cities he passed, gave us warning, and the comet with its tail had also been a warning. There was bread enough in our granaries (Petrus Leonis had seen to that, as formerly in the time of the siege), and Johannes Frangipane was ready to defend our walls. After the fire of the Normans, these had been rebuilt and formed a solid rampart; yet it was not behind them, but with open gates that we had to negotiate with the King.

The fact is that our other captains (they had been waiting a long time for the opportunity to overthrow Johannes Frangipane and Petrus Leonis) suddenly rose up in their castles and strongholds, as in the days of the great Crescentius and the Dux Alberic, exclaiming: "Our City was glorious and triumphed over all the peoples of the earth, long before there were any Popes: it is for us alone to bestow the Emperor's crown! Leave the negotiations to us! The King shall swear to maintain our rights, and we will then promise him the crown. And he will show his gratitude by ridding us of those two." (They meant Johannes Frangipane and Petrus Leonis.)

They then chose as their representatives (with a unanimity they rarely showed, being usually at variance with each other) the two Counts of Tusculum and Stephanus Normannus; these three then left for Arezzo to meet the Emperor, whom they addressed thus:

"What are your three thousand knights that you have brought with you? In our soil sleep the legions of nations. Swear then to maintain the rights of our City of Rome, for she is high above all dominion that you could possess outside of her!"

Whereupon the King (with deep cunning, for he was anxious to enter the City as quickly as possible and without striking a blow; also he would have liked to make sure of all of us at once): It aroused a deep feeling of reverence in him to be reminded of all the illustrious dead that lay buried in the dust of Rome; still there was no need to wake their shades, since their descendants and living images were now standing there before his very eyes. For the rest, he was come with the express purpose of rendering homage to their glorious City.

Accordingly, Stephanus Normannus and the two Tusculans returned to Rome and declared: "This man is not like the other princes who crossed the Alps before him, but he knows what is due to us. It behoves us therefore to give him the crown."

And thus it is that we had to negotiate with the King with open gates.

The chronicle relates:

We ourselves were not in the Church of St. Peter, when the Salian proceeded thither for his coronation; but we stood with our garlands and our banners on the bridge of S. Angelo, singing our hymns, as he passed. We could not see his face, however, for the Germans enveloped him in a cloak of swords, so to speak, as if they were accompanying him to battle, instead of to his crowning.

The Germans presented a magnificent sight; as they trooped down from the Mons Malus, they looked like a squadron of Archangels descending to earth. The fair hair under their steel helmets glittered like flax in the sun; all our captains struck one as almost brown beside them.

These latter also marched by with a numerous following, led by Frangipane, who did not want it to appear as if the others had already thrust him aside. Petrus Leonis alone rode almost without escort, although sumptuously arrayed, and having the appearance of some distinguished ambassador from foreign parts. The Germans, on seeing him, called out that he ought to have a star carried in front of him, as was done in their country on the 6th of January, when they dressed up as the Magi. Our illustrious Consul seemed quite flattered by this remark, for he was casting benevolent smiles in all directions. (But at that time the people still loved him, for he was generous to the poor—though always in prudent measure, so that his charity should neither harm the recipient nor lessen his own wealth.)

THE chronicle relates:

After this, when our captains and the great nobles of the King had entered the church, the Germans formed a vast chain all round the basilica and the portico of St. Peter's, as if an iron serpent were unrolling its rings, so that no one could depart or enter. (Some of our urchins who tried to slip through, had their ears pinched by the horsemen until they howled.) The serpent lay there for several hours.

Meanwhile we were still standing on the bridge, waiting for the bells to ring out to announce the coronation. But everything remained silent, only the serpent glowed and glistened, white at midday and grey in the afternoon. But when, as evening drew on, it was changing to a bluish tint, it suddenly started moving. We then perceived that the illustrious Consul Petrus Leonis, with his tiny escort (passing as it were between the feet of the serpent) was trying to make his way towards the bridge, like a man who hurries away from matters that do not concern him.

The Germans who stood near us (it was where the serpent ended): "Let him pass; one can see he is not a Roman Captain, but a foreigner."

At that moment a great tumult arose in the portico of St. Peter's, and when we pushed forward to see what was happening, the horsemen forced us back, calling out: "There is no Coronation! Our King has been betrayed! The Bishops refuse to give up the Regalia!" But suddenly they drew their swords, shouting: "It is not we, but the lord Frangipane who began it! Yes, the captains are traitors as well!"

FROM the archives of our golden city of Rome:

Some of us then ran in terror to the woman Susa, for we knew that she could get into the basilica of St. Peter's in spite of the horsemen.

She was just returning from Sancta Maria, muffled up to the chin in her great black cloak, so that her small face was almost lost to view.

We: "Mother Susa, can you tell us what is happening in St. Peter's?"

She: "I have just come from there. Everything is over."

One of the urchins, whom the Germans had pulled by the ear: "Aha, mother Susa, if you were in St. Peter's, the Germans must also have got hold of you by the ear."

Whereupon we dealt with the imp in the German fashion.

THIS is what the woman Susa then told us:

Our Holy Father, when the Salian had him surrounded so as to hold him captive, was in truth quite free. And when his own bishops abandoned him, then Christ our King came to him.

And He said: "Behold, I am about to be betrayed with you for thirty pieces of silver."

Then Our Savior passed through the midst of the knights of the Salian who sought to hold the Holy Father captive, and the Holy Father followed Him. But the knights did not see Our Savior; as the Holy Father was moving alongside of them, they thought he was following them.

The woman Susa was still speaking, when the first riders of Petrus Leonis appeared galloping over the Forum, shouting to everyone whom they met: "The Holy Father, together with all the Cardinals and the Captains, has been taken prisoner by the Salian! No one has escaped save the illustrious Consul; he summons the Civitas Romana to arms!"

The next morning, before daybreak, the people drove the Salian out of the Leonine Gate; without boots or stockings, he threw himself on his horse and galloped off at top speed. But he took his prisoners with him and did not release them until he had forced our Holy Father, by keeping him in cruel confinement, to give him the crown together with the Investiture.

But all this while our people would rally round no one save Petrus Leonis. And thus it was he came to be called "The King of Rome."

THE chronicle relates:

When the Salian was conducted for the second time to St. Peter's to be crowned, no bells pealed in our city, no hymns were sung, none of us stood with garlands and banners on the bridge of S. Angelo, but it was deathly still in all our streets, as if Rome lay under an Interdict; only in the back alleys, the people still shouted in their fury: "Long live the King of Rome!" Most of us were on our knees in the churches, praying, but some of us went again to the woman Susa.

She was seated in front of the church of Sancta Maria on the ancient Forum of the Romans, and she spoke of the Imperial Crown.

The woman Susa: "There are three Crowns instituted upon earth; all other crowns are in truth only circles, for those who wear them rule over this land or that, but the real crowns signify crowns in heaven and upon earth.

"The first crown is the triple crown with which our Holy Father is crowned. The second crown is the crown of Constantine, with which the Emperor is crowned. The third crown is the crown of thorns, with which every Christian is crowned. Woven into the crown of the Pope and into the crown of the Emperor is at all times a sprig from the crown of thorns; it is by that that we recognize them as sacred crowns. The greatest glory of the Papal crown is that it is the crown of Christ upon earth; but the greatest glory of the Imperial crown is to protect that other. When a humble man wears the Imperial crown, it shines resplendent; when a proud man wears it, it grows dim; but when someone steals it, or would take it by force, it is extinguished."

The woman Susa then added: "Let us pray once again that the Imperial crown be not extinguished."

All this while the sun had shone bright in the heavens; but on a sudden everything became black, as if night had descended.

The woman Susa (rising, pale as a dying woman who is passing to

her damnation): "King Henry has just been crowned in St. Peter's—
there is now neither Crown nor Emperor more!"

THE chronicle relates:

During the night following King Henry's coronation—it is known
among us as the accursed or the black coronation—a great snorting
of horses and hubbub were heard in many of our streets, as though
squadrons of cavalry were scouring the city from one end to the other,
so that we all jumped up from our beds, thinking that the Salian had
returned. (For he had rushed away immediately after the coronation
as if pursued by Furies.) The next morning, however, we talked with
those who had been in the streets during the night and had met the
horsemen. And this is what they told us: It was not squadrons of cavalry we had heard, but only four single horsemen, one mounted on a
red horse, another on a black one, the third on a grey one, just as St.
John the Evangelist has described them in his mysterious Apocalypse.
But the rider at the head of them, who was mounted on a white horse,
had cried out:

"Away! Away! Begone! Begone! For Antichrist is about to arise!
Woe to Christendom! Woe to the Pope of Rome: there is now no Imperial sword to protect them!"

Shouting and yelling in this way they had dashed through the Via
Lata, over the Tiber Bridge, and into the Leonine City towards the
Basilica of St. Peter's, which lay helpless and deserted, and with its doors
wide open, since those who had assisted at the black coronation had
forgotten in their horror to close them.

But on the steps of the Basilica they had been confronted by two
men, one holding in his hand a key, and the other a sword; at sight of
them the four riders had fallen down at the foot of the steps with a hollow thud, and the earth had seemed to engulf them. But from within its
bowels one had heard them yelling and raving for a long time: "We shall
return! We shall return!" until at last the two holy apostles had stamped
out the cry with their feet.

From that day we have all believed that Antichrist is to come in these times in which we live.

THIS is what we know about Antichrist:

There stands at the center of the world a human form (the center of the world, as we believe, is our City of Rome). Above the head of this figure hangs a ray, which is broken and falls like a stripe over its eyes. In its arm rests a staff, which is likewise broken. The feet of the figure are covered with the blood it has shed through the ages. But there is no earth beneath its feet, for it has no home, being like a tree that has its roots in no earthly kingdom. The bosom of this figure is filled with gold, and there the avaricious and violent in all lands slake their evil lust. But in its countenance, the haters and mockers slake the lust of their evil tongues. Now from this figure a child will issue; and this child when it reaches manhood, will crucify Our Lord Jesus Christ for the second time, that is to say, in the body of His Holy Church, wherein He moves upon earth. But this crucifixion will be known as the Great Schism or the real Schism of the West, namely the Schism of Antichrist.

It was not the woman Susa who told us this, but we have known it all our lives, having learned it from our fathers and mothers in early infancy. And our fathers and mothers had it from their fathers and mothers.

THE chronicle relates:

With the coronation of King Henry, the period of probation imposed by Holy Church on Petrus Leonis came to an end; for from that day the Curia of the Holy Father said in regard to him: He received St. Peter into his house (namely, the Holy Father Urban); afterwards he protected the City of St. Peter (namely, during the captivity of the Holy Father Paschal); accordingly he too must have his place in the house and in the city of St. Peter.

Certainly the Curia of the Holy Father did not say this at the top of its voice, so to speak, but as is its wont in saying these things, with a discreet moderation, like an anxious mother who knows she has many unreasonable and jealous children; but she said it, nevertheless, so that all could understand, and especially Johannes Frangipane. For this reason we call the day of King Henry's coronation the second great triumph of Petrus Leonis over Frangipane.

THE chronicle relates:

Meanwhile there was thunder and lightning in all the skies of Christendom: First of all, King Henry was excommunicated by the legates in Germany; next he was excommunicated by the legates in France and England; and soon afterwards, the Archbishop Guy of Vienne excommunicated him with Bell, Book and Candle. The Holy Father Paschal, however, did not excommunicate him.

But at that time there were many rebellious spirits in the Church, who said: The danger of the coming of Antichrist proceeds not only from the abdication of the temporal sword, but the spiritual sword also has become blunted. The real evil is not this heretical King of the Germans, but the sorrowful fact that we behold today an heretical Pope in the See of Peter. (They said this because of the Investiture which the Holy Father had granted to King Henry under the cruel stress of his confinement in the Castle of Trebico; for lay Investiture is equivalent to simony, and simony is heresy.) These voices became, alas, louder and more violent every day; but there were those among us who said: Investiture is not heresy at all, but only a sinful act; but it is heresy to characterize the Pope as a heretic, for that is contrary to the teaching of the Church. The Pope acted under duress, and therefore cannot justly be called to account.

Among the younger clergy of Rome, none defended this point of view with such zeal and address as the young Petrus Pier Leonis.

THE young Petrus Pier Leonis.

The chronicle relates:

He had just then returned from France, wearing the illustrious habit of the Order of Cluny, and equipped with the theological knowledge of the renowned school of Paris and of the great Petrus Abelard, at whose feet he had sat. The writings of this master used to come over the Alps in bulky packages; but those of us who read them said that the work from which one could best learn to understand and appreciate the famous Palace dialectician was the brilliant mind of the young Petrus Pier Leonis. His companions from Paris related that his fellow students there had given him the nickname of "Magister Petrus the second," because he had been the only one who was sometimes able in disputation to overcome the proud intellect of Abelard, in such a way, that is to say, that the latter himself admitted his defeat; for when others overcame him, as happened from time to time, they did so by appealing to the authority of revelation and the doctrine of the Church; but the master refused to recognize such victories, as he held the opinion that the times of simple submission by Faith had now passed, and that henceforward one must accept as true only what one could discern and grasp with the keen powers of the mind.

At this we asked: But why should the young Petrus Leonis, who is a disciple of Abelard, enter the lists against him?

They then told us that the young Petrus was wont to defend his master when he was attacked (already the latter had many bitter opponents), and to attack him when others agreed with him; for such was his keenness of intellect that a thesis he propounded one day he could refute the next with equal facility, and always with such logical force that it was impossible to find a flaw in his argument. His dialectical skill was truly amazing, and he had given many exhibitions of it to the great delight of the whole school.

Whereupon one of us, who had hitherto been silent: "If this be so, he may well have vanquished his master Abelard in brilliant fashion; but it merely means that the arguments he is now bringing to the controversy regarding King Henry's privilege have neither truth nor weight, and he would do better to remain silent before the least of the old women of Monte Caprino." (Even they had now begun to wrangle about the Investiture.)

But the Fathers of Saint Alexius said: "In this love for the innocent and the attacked we recognize our former pupil. And herein lies his truth."

EXTRACT from the notes of the Cardinal-Bishop Petrus of Portus (he had been kept prisoner with the Holy Father in the Castle of Trebico):

...But the world was not redeemed through those who take the part of the innocent (albeit we should always take the part of the innocent), but it was redeemed through the bitter Passion of the Innocent One. And daily I ask myself before God Who is all knowledge and all truth, whether I ought to tell of what really passed in the Castle of Trebico, and of the promises which the Holy Father there extracted from the Salian, or whether, if I did so, I might not immolate a great victim. For although our Holy Father is daily assailed by a storm of voices which blow down upon him like a hurricane from the North and East and West of Christendom, he himself maintains an unshakable silence, equally to those who accuse him as to those who would defend him.

But my days are numbered, and if I am silent today, I know not but that tomorrow my lips may be closed for ever upon this earth. May God make it known, if He will it otherwise. I will here write down what it has been given me to know of the hidden sanctity of our Holy Father. (I do not speak of the sanctity which belongs to every Pope in title of his office, but I speak of the saint in his person.)

It has been said: our Holy Father acted under constraint; but I say: there was a mystery in this constraint, and it was this: the Salians know our Popes. When all of us who were languishing in the Castle of Trebico implored the Holy Father on our knees to save the suffering Church by a provisional surrender of the Investiture, and to have mercy not only on the people of Rome who were bleeding in our cause, but also on the souls of the Germans who remained true to their King in blind loyalty, then undoubtedly we acted under the tyrannical pressure put upon us by that cruel king; but as regards our Holy Father himself, he acted in complete freedom, in the freedom, that is, of an accepted martyrdom. This is not to be understood as meaning that he gave his consent to that evil thing, the Investiture; but he consented to be the victim of an abuse of power, after the example of Our Lord Jesus Christ, in the hope that he might in this way snatch the king's heart from the gates of Hell at the very last moment, as it were, and move it to relinquish its godless design. But I myself did not realize this at first, but only later, when my eyes had been opened.

After the Holy Father had conceded that privilege to the Salian—he did it with tears in his voice and with upraised hands, as when one calls down the mercy of Almighty God—we received a message from the German Chancellor informing us that we were free to leave the Castle of Trebico at once and to proceed wheresoever it pleased us. But no sooner had we assembled in our travelling cloaks, each one issuing from his dungeon in a state of abject misery, and some of us positively ill from rage and bitterness, than we suddenly heard the short quick step of the Salian outside the door once again (no one who has once heard this step can fail to recognize it; it sounds like the blow of a hammer on the flagstones).

The Salian entered and addressed our Holy Father: As a sign of the sincere agreement which had been arrived at to their mutual satisfaction (it was in these ironical terms that he expressed himself), would the Holy Father give him his blessing before leaving, and in such a way that no future curse would be able to undo it? (He meant by this a promise that the Holy Father would never place him under the ban.)

While the King was speaking, we saw behind him, through the open door, some of his knights making signs to the men to lead away the horses that stood there waiting for us. We then realized that without this promise we were to be kept prisoners, and that it was perfectly true what one of our brothers said, with bitter mockery, in speaking of this king: namely, that he wrestled with our Holy Father, as Jacob had done with the angel, refusing to let him go, until the latter had blessed him.

Our blood ran cold, and we said in our hearts: This blessing will be invalid like the rest, having been extorted by fraud and violence; it will be a brigand's booty, which we must find means to recover at the first opportunity (for it was in this way that we had previously consoled ourselves in regard to the Privilege).

But the devil illumined the mind of the Salian, as if he had heard the voices of our secret conscience: we saw his face light up with a malignity of cunning which was not his own.

Going to the door, he called out to the knights who had ordered our horses to be led away: "Leave the horses there, so that our 'illustrious guest' (he adopted the same ironical tone as before) may depart." Then, turning to the latter: "Should you not wish, in view of what has happened, to give us your blessing, Holy Father, you may depart just the same, at your own good pleasure."

At this we all rose to our feet and made a hurried move to get away from this wicked Castle of Trebico with all possible speed; but at that moment the countenance of our Holy Father became transfigured as with the light of a supernatural pity, so that it was as if a halo of suffering and love encircled his venerable grey head. We saw him and heard him, hardly able to believe our ears and eyes the while, bestow his blessing upon this foreign, barbarian King, of his own free will as upon his worst enemy, like a father who draws to the heart the son who has ill-treated him.

Then the tears streamed from my eyes, for I realized that it was our Holy Father's will to break this King with the love of Christ, whereas we had believed that he himself, like the rest of us, had been broken on the hardness of this King's heart. (But such, I doubt not, had been our Holy Father's intention in regard to him from the beginning.) Moreover, I believe that our Holy Father hoped to the last that the King would throw himself at his feet, that is to say, at the feet of Christ, whose love he had seen revealed in him, renouncing the impious coronation and the rights he had so fraudulently obtained; nay, I do not hesitate to assert that at the moment when the crown was raised over King Henry's head, our Holy Father still hoped to see this miracle accomplished through the love of Christ. But with regard to this love, it is as our great Pope

Gregory VII has said: it wills to suffer for the sins of this world unto the end of time.

Written on the Feast of St. Jerome, Father of the Church, the day on which it has been resolved to convene the great Synod in the Lateran.

THE Synod in the Lateran.

(From the notes of the Cardinal-Bishop Petrus of Portus.)

...Afterwards, when we were all assembled in the great Aula of the Lateran Palace, with the Bishops ranged on either side along the glittering mosaics of the walls, mitre to mitre, these last resembling two long rows of white tulips, the Holy Father ascended the marble throne whereon the great Pope Gregory VII had sat, when he excommunicated the late King Henry. But away in a corner of the hall there still stood the empty throne of Agnes, the queen-mother, beside which she had knelt, when that ban was pronounced, weeping tears of humility before the Synod and the sentence passed by the Holy Father on King Henry, her son.

When we had recited the great prayers of the Introit and earnestly implored the help of the Holy Spirit, the Holy Father invited the Bishops to state their reasons for wishing him to convene this Synod.

Thereupon the first Bishop rose and made a formal protest against the Privilege, which he denounced as heretical; he then called upon the Holy Father to withdraw it and to trample Satan under foot, in other words, to excommunicate the cruel and godless tyrant, King Henry.

Then the second Bishop rose and spoke in the same sense.

After him the third got up and spoke, and then the fourth, and so on through the whole three hundred Bishops who composed the Synod. (But they all thought that the Holy Father had previously acted under compulsion.)

At the end the Holy Father Paschal rose and spoke: "We ourselves know as well as our brothers here assembled that this Privilege was a mistake (but he did not say why); nevertheless we do not wish to excommunicate King Henry, our son, for we have addressed a question to him which shall follow him to the end of his days. Let the Synod do then what seems to it salutary and right according to the Canons."

The Bishops thereupon withdrew the Privilege and excommunicated King Henry.

But meanwhile the Holy Father Paschal sat there, with head bowed under the weight of his tiara, and eyes fixed on the corner of the hall where once Queen Agnes had wept for her son; in his countenance was tenderness and peace, the overflowing gentleness of his Pastorate to which it bore witness, seeming in some sort to have poured the flood of its charity over himself (for he knew well that they thought he had defaulted), but to have poured it likewise over those who had pronounced the ban (for he knew also that they could not do otherwise). Many have since maintained that at that moment only the man was visible in his countenance, and not the Pope; but this is a grave error. For the suffering Church and the judging Church are not two but one, even as Christ, who suffered for the world, will one day judge it. But those who judge also suffer, and those who suffer are at the same time the judgment....

However, we know that he who spoke the bitter words: "King Henry has wrestled with our Holy Father Paschal for his blessing, as Jacob did with the angel," added some years later: "But, like him, from the blessing of this angel, he has remained crippled all his life."

The author of this remark was none other than the Cardinal Legate Lambert of Ostia, by whom the Concordat of Worms was concluded. But that peace could not prevent the Great Schism; the House of Petrus Leonis had already risen too high for that.

V

THE well of Saint Johannes in Fonte (of which we have already written)…but at that time no more bubbling and tossing was heard among its stones, but in its depths all was still, as if under the water someone were spying or lying in wait.

THE Jews of Rome relate:

On the day when it became known in the house of the Rabbi Nathan ben Jechiel that the young Petrus Pier Leonis had sat at the feet of the great master Abelard, Miriam asked her father to take her daughter into his school, in order that she might be initiated into the study of the Talmud and so become capable of one day controverting her brother.

The Rabbi Nathan ben Jechiel: "It is not our custom to instruct our daughters in the Talmud, for great learning, say our masters, leads a woman astray."

Miriam: "But our masters also tell of the great Berusia, the daughter of the Rabbi Chananja, who taught behind a veil in the School of Tiberias."

The Rabbi: "If it is the Lord's will—praise be to Him—He can enlighten your daughter."

Miriam: "But if it is not the Lord's will—" (she was thinking, then it is we who must enlighten her).

The Rabbi, severely and in shocked tones: "If it is not the Lord's will, Miriam, His name be praised none the less!"

Miriam (urgently): "But it is the Lord's will, father, it is the Lord's will."

Then Rabbi Nathan ben Jechiel was silent before his daughter; he did not say that he would grant her request, but he revered her grey hairs and the martyrdom she had endured at the birth of her child.

THE Jews of Rome relate:

In those days Rabbi Elchanan came once again to Rome. We had not seen him for a very long time, for the Goyim will not suffer any Jews in the city of Jerusalem, and since they have established their kingdom there, our Spanish brethren must go to their graves without the dust of the holy earth.

There was now no sack in the passage outside the door, when Rabbi Elchanan took food with Rabbi Nathan ben Jechiel, and people from the Jewish quarter did not now steal in to examine the gold ingots and treasures, but they came to jeer at Rabbi Elchanan, because he had once put them to shame with the "Crown of David." It was those, namely, who were always saying: Wherefore should we spend our days for ever mourning for Jerusalem?

When Elchanan came out of the door, some of these asked him: "Tell us, Rabbi, do our brethren in Toledo sleep better or worse, since you put them to bed in Spanish earth?"

The Rabbi (his figure was still unbent despite all the years that had passed, and his countenance had remained unchanged, with the same huge nose leaping out of it like the bold curve of a blade): "Your dead brothers at Toledo do not sleep in Spanish earth, but they sleep in the earth of the Lord, their God, and in the ashes of their own heads: Jerusalem has been dispersed over all the peoples of the earth!"

They then began to mock him: They had heard all that before, they knew already that Israel lived in the dispersion! (But they did not know it in the sense that the Rabbi Elchanan meant, nor did any of us at that time; it was not until many years later that this meaning was made clear to us by his disciples.)

THIS is what we learned from the disciples of the Rabbi Elchanan:

The Jews of Rome relate:

Our masters teach: The Law is the wall which separates Israel from the nations; but Rabbi Elchanan has taught: The Law of Israel is the gate of the nations.

Our masters teach: When the time is fulfilled, Israel will return home and again offer sacrifice in the holy Temple at Jerusalem. But Rabbi Elchanan has taught: Israel will never return home, but she will be the sign and witness of the One God among the nations. The bloody sacrifice of the Temple has been transformed into the bloody sacrifice of a whole people.

Rabbi Elchanan did not teach this from the beginning, however, but only after the capture of the city of Jerusalem by the Crusading army. It has been said that he was the only Jew who escaped from the Holy City alive, a Christian having concealed him in the house until the swords of the Crusaders, drunk with blood, had as it were tumbled to the ground; and also that this Christian had prayed with Rabbi Elchanan for his deliverance, both calling on the God of Israel, whom the Christians also pray to.

(It is not true, however, that Rabbi Elchanan is the only Jew who escaped from Jerusalem, as we saw another in Rome some time later. Of this latter we say: He escaped into the land of vengeance. But of Rabbi Elchanan his disciples say: He escaped into the kingdom of love.)

THE Jews of Rome relate:

Meanwhile Miriam continued to implore her father to let Trophäea attend his school, until her persistence began to annoy him. At last, not knowing what to say to her (for even now he had not the heart to scold her), he resolved to take counsel with Rabbi Elchanan. No one stood higher in Rabbi Nathan's esteem than the Rabbi Elchanan.

The latter asked time to reflect and to pray; he then bade them lead Trophäea to him, that he might question her and try to discover the Lord's will in regard to her.

Trophäea had now reached womanhood, but her frame was slight and fragile, and as undeveloped as that of a quite young girl; her face seemed somehow closed, like a bud, as if kept back from its unfolding by the shadow of its own blind eyes; in these, which were always wide open, one still beheld only the child.

The Rabbi Elchanan in a kind voice: "Do you remember, Trophäea, that time when I opened my sack and you called out: 'Hey, I see the crown of King David'?"

Trophäea (gaily): "Yes, I remember it well and shall never forget it."

The Rabbi Elchanan: "What did the crown look like, Trophäea?" (He had hitherto believed, like everyone else, that with her cry she had only demonstrated her blindness.)

Trophäea: "The crown had wings that were like gold dust flying into all the winds."

The Rabbi Elchanan: "And what happened when the wings dropped?"

Trophäea: "Then all the dust knelt down with them."

At these words, Rabbi Elchanan was moved to tears; they ran down on to his large nose, as when dew falls on a sharp sword.

The Rabbi Elchanan: "Then in very truth you beheld the crown of King David; for the Lord said to our Father Abraham: 'In thee shall be blessed all the nations of the earth.'" But afterwards to Rabbi Nathan ben Jechiel he said: "You ought not to deny the holy doctrine to this maid, for the Eternal—praise be to Him—chooses as his servants whomsoever He will; the seeing and the unseeing, men and women, the wise and the foolish, the willing and the unwilling—they are all one in his sight."

The Rabbi ben Jechiel, shaking his head: "Why not go a step further, Rabbi Elchanan, and say: 'He also chooses the children of Edom'?"

At these words Rabbi Elchanan was greatly upset and went as white as the chalk on the wall; but Rabbi Nathan ben Jechiel was equally upset at having dared to impute so grave a sin to Rabbi Elchanan even in jest.

Rabbi Nathan ben Jechiel (to make amends): "Very well then, you teach Trophäea; for your sake, I am prepared to think it right."

The Rabbi Elchanan (still as white as the chalk on the walls): "No, teach her yourself, Rabbi Nathan!"

And so they continued to argue for a considerable time. But next morning Rabbi Elchanan departed from Rome secretly and without taking his leave.

After that Rabbi Nathan resolved to instruct Trophäea, for he said to himself: "In her I will make good the wrong I did to him."

THE Jews of Rome relate:

Before admitting Trophäea into his school, Rabbi Nathan ben Jechiel insisted that she should provide herself with a veil, like the great Berusia, who always appeared veiled in the school of Tiberias.

Miriam to her father: "Why should she, who is to be the consolation of us all, have to wear a veil? Is being a woman a thing to be ashamed of?"

The Rabbi Nathan ben Jechiel: "It is not to her dishonor that a woman wears a veil and conceals her face, but to her honor. For we recognize the strength of a fortress through the fact that its gates are shut. But woman is the last fortress of every people. If the man falls, God will punish the man; but if the woman falls, God will punish the whole people."

To which, Miriam: "She will not fall, and she will cause the fall of no man, for the Lord has already veiled her in her own countenance." (By this she meant that none of the young men at the school would desire her because she was blind.)

The Rabbi: "Yes, the Lord has veiled her, but He has also placed a crown upon her, and a day will come when she will be conscious of it. Remember your own youth, Miriam!"

Miriam: "I remember nothing, save that my daughter is to be her brother's sister!" In truth, Miriam had early resolved that Trophäea should never be the wife of any man, even if someone sought her in marriage despite her blindness.

At this the Rabbi (for he knew what Miriam was thinking): "If that is your wish, you ought to ask me to have her veiled not once, but twice. Know, however, that I am not having her veiled in order to further your plan; so far as that is concerned, the matter is in God's hands, and He alone will decide."

THE Jews of Rome relate:

And so Trophäea sat veiled in the school among the young men of Rome, and learned from Nathan ben Jechiel the sentences and maxims of our masters, which we do not set down in books. For we know that there should be only one book here upon earth, namely the holy Torah, which the Lord Himself wrote, and which it is not fitting to imitate in other books with the wisdom of men. This wisdom we transmit only from memory, so as to mark the great distance that separates it from the wisdom of the Lord. But it follows that we commit a great deal to memory, for the wisdom of men is also carefully preserved among us, that it maybe learned and passed on to our children.

But among the pupils of Rabbi Nathan, none had such a retentive memory as the blind daughter of Miriam.

THE Jews of Rome relate:

At school, when the young sons of Israel hesitated and stumbled, the Rabbi would turn to Trophäea, and behind her veil she always brought out with an eager, charming precision, the exact thought of the master, which the Rabbi wanted to hear, just as in the old days she had recited the sayings and canticles of the Prophets.

At that time our women used often to remark to each other: This blind girl is like a wax taper in her mother's hand: the latter ignites her will just as she pleases, and its flame is the light of her desires, for at present it has no desires of its own.

But already the taper was beginning to flicker in Miriam's hand.

THE women of the Jews relate:

Said Trophäea, the daughter of Miriam, to Hannah Naemi: "Auntie dear, describe to me what a bride looks like!" (This was the first time that Trophäea had asked what a thing looked like. Hitherto she had found delight only in the images she made in her own soul.)

Then Hannah Naemi led Trophäea to the chest in which Miriam preserved her bridal dress and her bridal ornaments. But she kept both only for the sake of the day on which she wore them to return to her father's house. Sometimes, when foreign Jews came to Rome and stayed with Nathan ben Jechiel, they asked to see Miriam's bridal dress.

Miriam would then open the chest and say: "This is the dress in which I was wedded to Israel, my people."

Then the foreign Jews would bow before Miriam, especially those from Spain, for in that country they had already begun to sing an epic chant about the daughter of Nathan ben Jechiel. (But there are some great poets among the Spanish Jews.)

Hannah Naemi, unfolding Miriam's bridal dress: "See, child" (she always said "see," when she meant "feel," so as not to destroy Trophäea's illusion), "this is the purple with which a bride clothes herself; it signifies the bride's love!"

Next she took from the chest the gold chains and rings; they clinked mysteriously in her hands.

Hannah Naemi: "See, here are the chains and rings they put on a bride; their gold signifies the bride's faithfulness."

She then took the crown out of the chest; it was beautifully curved like Miriam's brow.

Hannah Naemi: "See, this is the bridal crown; it signifies the bride's honor."

Finally Hannah Naemi took from the chest the veil with which Miriam had "covered" her head. It was sown all over with golden corn-seeds, in accordance with the invocation that is made when the veil is put on: "Be thy increase a thousandfold, Sister!"

Hannah Naemi: "See, child, this the veil with which a Jewish bride is covered on the day of her marriage; it signifies the bride's blindness!"

(She meant for all, save her husband.)

Trophäea, after she had felt every article very delicately with her fingers: "Auntie dear, what is blindness?"

THE women of the Jews relate:

In those days Trophäea began to bloom like a rose of Sion. Out of her slender frame was emerging in all its radiance the one-time beauty of her mother Miriam, as when in the spring time a flowering tree cradles its blossom above the narrow walls of its garden.

Trophäea to Hannah Naemi: "What do I look like, Auntie dear? Am I beautiful, or am I not? Tell me, how do people regard me? What do they say when they set eyes on me?"

This was the second time that Trophäea asked what something looked like.

THE women of the Jews relate:

About that time (and we knew very well why we did it) we began to tell Trophäea about the martyrdom that her mother had endured in giving her birth. But Trophäea refused to listen, and we saw by the look on her face that it inspired her with fear, nay horror.

Trophäea to Hannah Naemi: "Auntie dear, tell these women to keep quiet! I don't want to be the child of a martyr. Oh, what a horrible thing martyrdom is! Oh! how sad it is not to be like everyone else!"

THE women of the Jews relate:

Said Trophäea, the daughter of Miriam, to Hannah Naemi: "Auntie dear, please put a chain round my neck, when I go to school!"

Accordingly Hannah Naemi put a chain round her neck.

Said Trophäea, the daughter of Miriam, to Hannah Naemi: "Auntie dear, do please cut a little hole in the veil I wear at school, so that the others can see me!"

So Hannah Naemi cut a little hole in Trophäea's veil, just large enough to make her mouth visible.

Hannah Naemi, deep down in her old heart: God forgive me if I am doing wrong, but it is better that I should do wrong, than that a human creature should fret herself to death.

But the next morning, Trophäea said: "Close up the hole again, Auntie dear; it is no use letting others see me, since I can see nobody!"

THE Jews of Rome relate:

That day at the school, when Trophäea was repeating the words of the master who said: "When a man and a woman live together in holy union, the *Schechina* of the Lord rests upon them," she suddenly broke down, and could not continue.

The Rabbi sent her home, pretending that he wanted her to take a message to her mother; for he thought that she had forgotten the passage and was overcome with shame. But when he himself returned home soon afterwards and went to comfort her, he found her sobbing her heart out in her room.

Trophäea, as if crushed by despair: "Oh, why am I here? Why am I here? Tell me! I can no longer see anything, I can no longer see anything!"

The Rabbi left the room without a word; but he did not call Miriam, he went to Hannah Naemi.

The Rabbi Nathan ben Jechiel to Hannah Naemi: "She is blind, but she is beautiful, and if a worthy man desires her in marriage, I will give her to him; her mother can object as much as she likes."

He spoke to the same purpose among the men of the community. Miriam, however, declared: "I have dedicated her to the Lord, that she may do His wish; she has become His property like the daughter of Jephta."

Then the men of the community said to Rabbi Nathan ben Jechiel: "Yes, your granddaughter is indeed beautiful; but we are afraid of her beauty, for her mother has betrothed her to the angels, that she may do the work of the Lord; but the Lord has accepted her and put His seal upon her (by this they meant Trophäea's blindness). It would ill beseem us to break the seal of the Lord."

And so no one dared to solicit Trophäea in marriage.

THE women of the Jews relate:

It was a long time before Trophäea understood that she was to remain unmarried, and longer still before she became reconciled to the idea. Especially when she heard the voices of children, she was apt to become sad, and later even irritable. The children who played before the Rabbi's door, used sometimes to complain to their mothers that the Rabbi's granddaughter was very bad-tempered and always scolding them. A look of pity would then come over the faces of the Jewish women, and they would tell their children to go and play elsewhere, for although Trophäea now bore little trace of her former self, it was still as the devout child of the martyred Miriam that she continued to be regarded in the neighborhood. Only while everyone treated her with respect and tenderness because of the state to which she was predestined, she herself viewed that state with aversion, and her heart was filled with pain and bitterness.

THE Jews of Rome relate:

Trophäea's will stiffened against her destiny, but Miriam's will stiffened against her daughter.

Hannah Naemi to her niece (she remembered the golden shoes of the Senatrix Marozzia): "Miriam, have you forgotten that you yourself once desired a husband? And did you not adorn yourself from head to foot for his sake, and demand of his love a son that you might offer him to Israel?"

Miriam: "My daughter shall offer Israel a son; for that she has no need of a husband, but all she needs is to be ready every hour to obey the voice of the Lord when He calls. But she sets herself against the will of the Lord, and so the promise fails of its fulfillment. She is like our people who fell down in the desert before the idols of the heathen; hence it is that we do not enter Canaan."

But it was already the time when we said: "Miriam, when your son was yet a child, they dubbed him the 'Cardinal,' and now we hear that they are calling your one-time husband the 'King of Rome.' How can you still believe that your weak, blind daughter will ever triumph over such great men?"

Miriam in reply: "Before God no man is great."

VI

THE Chronicle relates: Petrus Leonis now stood at the height of his power. There existed in Rome no grander nor—as we thought—more Christian prince than he. All the pious folk among us said that in the days of the Salian he had proved himself the most trustworthy and most sagacious protector of our city and of the Holy Father. The people continued to call him the "King of Rome," and there were those who relied on his arm to save them in the event of Antichrist really appearing. Moreover, in clerical circles one frequently heard the view expressed that whenever a Jew was truly converted, the lost election of his race was once again renewed in him, in the sense, namely, that he became a special instrument of Providence. Father Aigidius of Saint Alexius developed this view in a voluminous tractate, adducing in support of it, among other examples, that of St. Paul, the Prince of the Apostles. This tractate he dedicated to the illustrious Consul Petrus Leonis.

Once, however, when the latter, loaded with honors and confidence, arrayed as it were in all the splendor of his acknowledged Christianity, was descending from the monastery of Saint Alexius, Pater Grammaticus cast after him a look of most sinister irony.

Pater Grammaticus to his brother monks: "Yes, Petrus Leonis has now established himself in a grand position with us, and has managed things exceedingly well; but what his actual feelings are, you can gauge from the conduct of his son. Indeed, if the latter had really taken roots in our soil, he would not now be championing the thesis of the *Gesta Dei per Francos*, for this thesis (at least as he understands it) contradicts the ordinances of Christ among the nations, and the Cross, which is laid upon our Holy Church, and which she has herself solemnly professed before every one of these Salian kings."

THE thesis of the *Gesta Dei per Francos*.

We went to see the woman Susa.

She has a small voice like that of a child, only rather more hollow; it is so thin and low that many of her hearers failed to notice when she uttered great sayings; but those who did notice it, always felt that one day her voice would break in giving them forth.

We: "Mother Susa, some while ago you said that the Imperial crown had been extinguished; but there are those who maintain that it will shine again, namely on the heads of the kings of France. It is they who will take upon themselves the earthly protection of the Holy See, and obtain the Empire."

She: "May God in His mercy prevent it!"

We: "You are a German, then, mother Susa, since you wish the Empire to remain with Germany?" As a matter of fact, she had not been born in our city, but had wandered to us a pilgrim from distant parts. We had long wanted to know the land she came from, but when we asked her, her reply was always the same: "I come to you from the great sins of the world, but I have now established myself here in the mercy of Christ." (By this she meant the Holy See.)

She: "If I were a German, it would be harder for me today to say what I know, though even then I could not do otherwise than say it; but it does not sound well when a person begins praising his own people. However, I come from the land of France, and I therefore have good right to praise Germany."

At this we all rejoiced, because we know that the land of France has produced many saints; but we should have liked to produce a living saint among ourselves.

THE woman Susa on the Germans.

She spoke as follows:

"In the land of France all pious Christians are now saying: Let us pray for the Germans, that their king may have his eyes opened; these people are indeed barbarians, but they are also strong and steadfast like no other people upon earth, and for this reason it was Christ's will to give them Empire just as he gave Priesthood to the Romans; to France, however, says an old proverb, is allotted Study. For the missions of peoples are not mere matters of chance, but just as the nations on earth have their princes, these likewise have theirs in Heaven, who are called 'Thrones or Dominations.' Like the angels, these are arranged in a hierarchy, and their diadems are not interchangeable; nor is it permitted to dispute about them on earth, but whenever such dispute arises, it must be taken as the precursive sign of Antichrist whose purpose is to tear heaven and earth apart."

But seated in our number was a man whom we all looked upon as a great lout because of his obstinate refusal to believe in the revelations of mother Susa.

This man: "So in your opinion, mother Susa, the person who is now putting forward the thesis of the *Gesta Dei per Francos*, is a forerunner of Antichrist?" (He knew, however, that this was no other than the young Petrus Pier Leonis, a consecrated priest, whom the Holy Father had just attached to the Curia. But the woman Susa did not know this.)

She gave a sudden start and shrank back with a shudder, as if an imperceptible wind had gripped hold of her (imperceptible, since we did not feel it); then, without saying a word, she fixed her interlocutor with her large pale eyes, got up and walked away.

We turned with fury on the man who had put the question: "Take care, or you yourself will be looked upon as a forerunner of Antichrist for frightening away our Saint! You had better not let it happen again! Mother Susa saw through you right enough, and gave you the answer you deserve; but next time we will answer you instead, and after that you won't be quite so ready with your questions."

At these words he made off as fast as he could, for he saw that some of us were getting ready to give him the kind of answer we meant, there and then.

Bellowing from a safe distance: "Just wait until the Church pronounces her decision on the *Gesta Dei*, and then you will see what your Saint is worth, and where she gets her inspiration!"

However, although Holy Church, out of gratitude to Petrus Leonis for his services, had attached his son to the Curia, she nevertheless opposed this thesis with unshakable resolution; until the day came when the Frangipani compelled her to accept it by the use of violence.

The Jews of Rome say of Petrus Leonis: "The Lord has so blinded the children of Edom, that they are playing into his hands." (They mean by this, the hatred of the Frangipani.)

From now on begins the great struggle between that family and the family of Petrus Leonis.

THE chronicle relates:

In those days, all the captains who had previously arranged for a delegation to be sent to King Henry at Arezzo, met together again. Among those present were the two Counts of Tusculum, the Crescentii, the three Corsi, the men-folk of Saint-Eustachius, Counts Johannes and Gozzelin of Galera, the Bericisi, and Stephanus Normannus accompanied by members of his family. They said to each other: "The Holy Father has been betrayed by the Salian. But the people and the Curia put the blame on us, because we allowed the King to enter the city. Henceforward they will trust no one but Petrus Leonis and honor no one but him. Yet in reality it is he who is the cause of the mischief, not we; for had it not been for his intolerable alliance with the Frangipani, we should never have promised the crown to King Henry at Arezzo. Petrus Leonis is to blame for everything, and we must rid ourselves of him as quickly as possible, that no new evil may betide."

Afterwards they resolved as a first move to detach Johannes Frangipane from Petrus Leonis by playing on the former's jealousy, for they felt that if they could do that they would be able to overcome the latter more easily.

THE chronicle relates:

One day Stephanus Normannus—he was very astute and self-composed—offered to accompany Johannes Frangipane to the Palace of Octavian. On the way he told him that they were saying in the Papal Curia that the old motto ought to be changed; it should no longer run: to hold together like the sword of Frangipane and the purse of Pier Leone, but: like the head of Pier Leone and the fist of Frangipane.

Stephanus Normannus said this not so much to remind Frangipane that the Curia regarded Petrus Leonis as a clever and level-headed man, as to let him know that they thought him unstable and something of a blockhead; and it was in this sense that Frangipane understood it; for he well knew that it was his violence that had first drawn the sword in the portico of Saint Peter's, and so given the knights of the Salian the excuse to draw theirs. Moreover, the tumult of Guibert of Ravenna was still a disturbing memory; and being mindful of the dubious part he had played therein, he resented it when others showed no disposition to forget it.

Frangipane, starting up with a vehemence that set all his arms jingling: "The Curia had better take care, or soon they will be saying: The sword of Frangipane or the head of Pier Leone!"

From that day onward the captains waited in daily expectation of hearing the cry of battle raised, but they waited in vain; for the great, the puissant Frangipane, however fiercely he might act before Stephanus Normannus, still lay with his two arms bound to precisely the same gold chain as before, his sword buried like a wretched bushel in a heap of red gold. But this heap of gold meant for him just then: the dowry of Tullia Pier Leone.

TULLIA Pier Leone.

When she was a child, Johannes Frangipane had always feared that she would be carried off prematurely like her brothers Obicione and

Guido. However, his fears had proved groundless, for she had reached womanhood and was now betrothed to Cencius Frangipane, the eldest son of Johannes. The latter had originally intended her for his second son, Leo, for although he had been gloating over the prospect of Tullia's dowry for years, he did not want, as he said, the blood of the heir of his house to be "corrupted" through her. The young Leo, however, when he learned that they intended reserving Tullia for him (he was hardly more than a boy at the time, and helpless in the hands of his violent father), crept into the cage of the leopard which the Frangipani kept for hunting, and before the eyes of his horrified father, put his arms round the wild beast's neck, crying out that he would rather be torn to pieces by the leopard than let himself be forced into a marriage with a girl who was not of Roman blood like himself.

This exploit, so it was said, convinced Johannes Frangipane that the blood of his second son was purer than that of the first, and he therefore betrothed Tullia Pier Leone to Cencius.

TULLIA Pier Leone.

She still wore, as in the days of her childhood, the hem of her dress adorned with little gold and silver bells, after the manner of the daughters of the Byzantine emperors. (Donna Bona, her stepmother, made a great point of this, for apart from herself and her daughters, there was no one in Rome who could have afforded to dress in this fashion.) The little bells tinkled charmingly about Tullia's slender ankles, but they clashed badly with the sad expression on her youthful face. The fact is that Tullia had often seen her mother redden when Johannes Frangipane pressed the question of the marriage (but Donna Bona reddened because she remembered why her own brothers had once been so pressing with regard to her own marriage). Petrus Leonis, on the other hand, remained quite unruffled, and did not turn red at his friend's importunity; for he always had ready a very excellent reason for postponing the marriage, and that was, that he was not yet in a position to pay down Tullia's dowry.

Johannes Frangipane (he stood squarely on his feet, but his face was all red and confused, and he could not look his friend in the eyes): "It is high time, Petrus Leonis, it is high time! We are getting on in years, and we want to be able to see our grandchildren."

Petrus Leonis: "Yes, we are getting on in years, Johannes Frangipane, and we need peace and union for the evening of our days." (He said this, because he well knew that Frangipane would rise up against him, as soon as he had secured Tullia.)

Meanwhile, the young Cencius rejoiced at the postponement of the marriage, for he abominated Tullia no less than did his brother Leo.

Cencius and Leo Frangipane.

They were both blond, and not browned over like the other captains, but like flax in the sun, white-golden like the Germans who lately descended from Mons Malus for the Coronation. Their skin was as clear and white as the skin of two maidens, and under the scorching heat of summer, it did not get bronzed, but mottled like the skin of the beautiful leopard which the young Leo had embraced. The eyes of both the Frangipani, however, were black, like the eyes of the Counts of Tusculum, whom we know to be descended from the Anici.

These latter often said to them: One can see from your skin and your hair, that you Frangipani are of barbarian stock. But the young Frangipani did not like to be told this, as they hated the Germans; though, truth to tell, they hated them only because they sought dominion over the city of Rome. Petrus Leonis, however, they hated in their blood.

The young Frangipani to the Counts of Tusculum: "We are well aware that a barbarian woman once married into our family. She can find no rest in her grave, and is doomed to reappear in all our faces; but our fathers are descended from the Julii as are yours from the Anici."

The Counts of Tusculum with their haughty Roman faces: "That is for you Frangipani to prove!"

The latter understood quite well what they meant, for the captains had now given up Johannes Frangipane and were placing all their hopes in his young sons.

THE chronicle relates:

The young Counts of Tusculum (the sons of the Counts who went to Arezzo) had formed a pact with a certain number of young men. These saluted each other, not as we do, with an inclination of the head, but by holding the arm outstretched—a vehement and striking form of salutation which they copied from our Pagan ancestors. But the word of greeting which accompanied this salute was the name of our city of Rome. At first people made fun of this invocation, and asked the young men whether they had nothing to say to each other but the name of the city in which they were born. Actually they had a great deal to say to each other, the burden of their talk being the evil condition we were in, the glory of our past greatness, and how that glory might be restored to us. But when we asked them on what they placed their hopes, whether they were Imperialists, Papalists or Lombardists, they shook their heads in vigorous denial.

We: "What then do you want, you Tusculans? What are you?"

They: "We want Rome, we are Romans and nothing else!"

THE chronicle relates:

Behind the Palace of the Tusculans lies a garden among the remains of some old Pagan ruins. There are tall trees in the garden with a richness of foliage and shade such as is to be found in no other spot in Rome; for the ancient waters still trickle there from the time of our Pagan forefathers who used to come and bathe there. Under the trees stands a sarcophagus, of beautiful workmanship, but sinfully decorated with the naked figures of gods and goddesses, whose heads are intoxicated with the juice of the grapes they are plucking from the trailing vine. This sarcophagus was placed there by the young Counts of Tusculum and their friends; on its lid may be seen each morning a wreath of laurels and roses which the young men laid there during the night. (They pretend that in the sarcophagus lies buried the glory of Rome.) Sometimes they spread a black pall over it, and stand round it in a circle with torches in their hands; these they then extinguish before the sarcophagus with solemn gestures of grief. They performed this rite on the day the Germans entered our city, and again later, when they learned that Petrus Leonis had been acclaimed King of Rome.

THESE are the words which the young Counts of Tusculum and their friends pronounce, as they extinguish the torches:

"Oh Rome, once thou wast the head and crown of the earth, and now thou art the prey of fierce barbarians and greedy usurers! But we, we will be thy prey: Rome our queen, Rome our mother, Rome our bride! Rome, who canst not die, grant that we may die for thee! Rome, of whose shame we die, grant that we may live for thee!"

THE chronicle relates:

When the young Counts of Tusculum spoke of Petrus Leonis, they never mentioned him by name, but referred to him as "he," and everyone in their organization understood whom they meant.

The young Counts of Tusculum: "How can we hope to keep the Germans away from Rome, our queen, when we cannot even overcome 'him'?" (The young Frangipani, however, knew that the whole nobility pointed accusingly at their father as the man who had made "him" the power he was.)

The young Frangipani: "'He' managed to climb up on our backs, but we know where we belong!"

The Tusculans once more: "Then prove it, you Frangipani!"

FROM the archives of our golden city of Rome.

The chronicle relates:

The family of the Frangipani started open hostilities against Petrus Leonis on the death of the Prefect of the city, when the Roman people wished to elevate Petrus Leonis to that office. (The Prefect is the chief criminal judge of our city.)

In those days we began to hear it said for the first time that there was something dubious about the family of the Pier Leoni, and that a stain still clung to it on account of its Jewish origin (hitherto we had believed that a special grace lay upon the few members of that obstinate race who from time to time were converted to Christ). In taverns and in the public places of the city, one met persons of all kinds who loudly proclaimed that the race of the Jews was cursed among all the nations of the earth and that nothing good could ever come out of it. We knew, however, that these persons had been sent out by Johannes Frangipane, and when he himself fell ill, as happened about this time, it was commonly said in the city that the illness he was suffering from was his rusty sword (the sword that he could not draw, because Tullia still remained unmarried). Meanwhile the Holy Father Paschal paid not the slightest attention to this unchristian talk about the impossibility of any good coming out of the Jewish race, and let it be known that he was willing to confirm the choice of the Roman people.

It was then that the two young Frangipani spoke to their father the famous words: "Here, father, serpents are of no avail, but only swords."

At the same time they informed him that they had mortgaged the whole of their maternal heritage in order to promote a rising against Petrus Leonis; this was demanded by the honor of their family, and the whole nobility of Rome expected it of them.

Johannes Frangipane, frightened to death: "You young fools! You cannot raise an insurrection against Petrus Leonis with your mother's fortune alone, you will fail miserably."

They: "Then we will fail, but we cannot go back." They had kept their enterprise secret from their father until the last moment, in order to compel him to join them, for they knew themselves that if they acted alone they were both lost; they wanted further to see their father's name as well as their own restored to honor among the nobility.

When Johannes Frangipane saw that it was too late to put a stop to the plan, and that—unless he wished to drive his own flesh and blood to destruction—he must throw in his lot with them, he suggested that Cencius should carry off Tullia by force, in order to secure her dowry whatever happened. The two youths did not reply, for they felt ashamed of their father.

Tullia's Dowry.

The chronicle relates:

On the evening fixed for the rising, the Frangipani gave a great banquet, to which they invited Tullia, and also her young brothers, the sons of Donna Bona. Two of these, Jordanus and Leo, were still children, but Gratianus, Niccolaus, Roger and Romanus were already grown up, and so they accompanied their half-sister Tullia to the banquet.

They danced the *ezzelina*; this dance derives its name from a beautiful lady of Forli, who invented it. The young maidens all joined in, for Johannes Frangipane was a widower and there was no woman in his house to watch over the proprieties. The *ezzelina*, however, ought properly speaking only to be danced in the meadows, for it is a very spirited dance which proceeds at a running step and requires a wide space for its vigorous, almost violent evolutions. The doors of the dance room were wide open, the dancers continuing their wild motions in the galleries and corridors and through all the rooms of the house until they reached the towered chamber above the Arch of the seven-branched candlestick (here the palace of Johannes Frangipane ends). Only Tullia Pier Leone had no mind to dance through the tower; she said the damp walls had such a musty smell that it made her feel ill.

The guests to each other, behind Tullia's back: "One would think her blood had suddenly remembered its origin. Don't they say that no Jew will pass through the Arch of the seven-branched candlestick?"

Tullia's garland hung like a faded creeper in her slate-colored hair; this was because she kept on clutching at it with her hands, for fear it should slip off without her knowing it.

Jacoba Frangipane (she was still unmarried, and continued to live in her uncle's house; she could not abide Tullia as being the sister of the young Petrus to whom she had once so vainly offered her ring): "Why do you keep on fiddling with your garland? It sits firmly enough—it is not yet your wedding, is it?"

Jacoba had decked herself out with all her jewels for the evening; but this did not make her ugly features any the more prepossessing, but only slightly pathetic, since it was obvious to everyone that she was trying hard to make herself attractive to someone who took no interest whatever in her beautiful hands. (She was in love with her cousin Cencius.) The latter danced with her the whole evening so as not to have to dance with Tullia. Leo Frangipane, however, did not dance at all, but stood outside on the balcony waiting for the signal (for on this same night the Frangipani were to sally forth).

Tullia Pier Leone, pulling herself up with a sudden jerk in the middle of the room, so that all the little bells on her dress tinkled furiously: "Where are my brothers? Where are my brothers? I don't see them any more! Does anyone know where they are?" But no one could give her any information, for the young Pier Leoni had secretly taken their departure, each thinking that one of the others had told their sister and taken her away with him.

Truth to tell, from the beginning of the evening, a rumor had spread among the guests: "Give heed that nothing happens before the night is out." (Only too often something happens at our banquets, and many times have we seen swords and death amid the dancing and the feasting!) In addition, the women and young maidens felt eerie because from the palace of the Frangipani one can see the ancient Forum of the Romans, and this is wild and melancholy like no other place on earth. Nevertheless, during the pauses they could not resist going on to the balcony to watch the lights which at night circulate there boldly amid the ruins. Among them was one which moved about high up in the Palace of the Caesars; one saw it flicker from room to room, as if someone were carrying a torch in the wind through the whole palace. (But we know that these lights are the spirits of Pagans that gather around Sancta Maria de Inferno.)

Meanwhile Tullia, who was becoming increasingly alarmed, kept on calling for her brothers.

Jacoba Frangipane: "They are probably in the big hall drinking wine with my uncle. Go down and see, Tullia." (But she said it without conviction, for she too was beginning to feel that something was going to happen, but she did not know what, and was afraid of spoiling anything her family might have in hand.)

Tullia, however, did not go down; a sudden fear of all the doors gripped her, and she insisted on standing in the center of the room beneath the torches. (These, however, had almost burned themselves out, for the feast was nearing its end.)

At that moment the voice of Johannes Frangipane was heard at the foot of the staircase, calling his son Cencius.

Cencius was now standing on the balcony. Leo had already received his signal and had quietly ridden off.

Johannes Frangipane, going up to Cencius (he was twice as big and broad as his son): "Why are you standing here gazing at the night? Don't you see that your bride is waiting for you?" (He meant by this that it was high time to dance Tullia away into one of the back rooms; after which the door would be shut behind them. That had been Johannes Frangipane's plan.)

Suddenly one of the women gave a loud shriek, for it looked as though the young Cencius were about to throw himself from the balcony. (He did not do so, however, because Johannes Frangipane remembered in time his son Leo in the leopard's cage.)

Johannes Frangipane, leaving his son, in a voice which sounded almost gentle: "Very well, I myself will dance with Tullia." He then moved towards her.

Pale as death the young Cencius sprang forward and rushed past his father.

Tullia, pushing Cencius away with her hands: "I will not dance any more! I will not dance any more! The dancing is all over."

Cencius Frangipane: "It will be in a moment." To the musicians who had already ceased playing: "The *ezzelina*!" He then caught hold of Tullia and started dancing with her.

The others likewise continued dancing (though for how long they were afterwards unable to say).

Once again a loud cry suddenly arose from one of the women: "Stop,

Cencius, Tullia cannot go on!" Little did she know then that he had been dancing with Tullia the whole time without a break, for the others had changed partners several times and rested. But she suddenly noticed that the wild measures of the *ezzelina* were always a half-beat behind Cencius, so rapidly was he dancing. Tullia, on the other hand, was hardly dancing at all: the little bells hung torn from her dress, her mouth was like an open wound in a dying face.

Now from all sides they shouted to Cencius to leave off; some even tried to hold him back, but they could not catch him. Moreover, by this time the torches had nearly all gone out, and darkness was invading the room.

Then as though seized with a sudden stupor the whole company stood still (for they had just realized what was happening). The musicians realized it too: the music went pale, staggered and broke off like a desolate cry.

The last torch had gone out: the lights of the Pagans that flitted about over the Forum outside broke into the room and enveloped the dancers.

Johannes Frangipane, who alone still dragged his heavy body after the frenzied dancer (he did not see the lights of the Pagans), brandishing his sword and panting with fury: "This is not dancing, Cencius, it is murder!"

Cencius Frangipane: "Better murder than shame!"

At the same moment a human body fell to the ground in the darkness. But it was not Tullia Pier Leone, it was Johannes Frangipane, whose rage had brought on a stroke.

The chronicle relates:

Meanwhile the palace of the city Prefect had been surrounded by Leo Frangipane. They dragged from his bed the young son of the deceased (for it was he who was to raise the cry of battle), burst open the iron chest where the robes and sword of the Prefect were kept, and threw over the astonished youth the silken dalmatic of his father. Then they rushed him into the latter's colored breeches, one leg red and the other gold (for such is the costume worn by the Prefect of Rome), cocked the tall mitre on his head, and put the heavy pummel of the naked sword in his tender hand. After which they hoisted the resisting boy like a dressed up doll on to the back of a horse—the breeches being far too large for him hung like two empty sacks over the animal's flanks—and rode off with him at a gallop, with Leo Frangipane in front, his blond hair waving under his helmet like a pennon unfurled in the dawn.

With horns blowing and torches flashing they drew up outside the palace of the Tusculans. These from their balcony: "Aye, you have now made good your words, you Frangipani! You have now proved yourselves! We salute your blond ensign, you are of pure blood notwithstanding!"

The young Leo (his arm stretched forth in salutation in the manner prescribed by their pact) with jubilant voice: "Rome! Rome!"

They then pursued their way to the castle of Pier Leone: here Johannes and Cencius were to wait for them. They were not waiting for them, however.

Leo Frangipane: "Very well, then, we will not wait for them either. Lead forth the Prefect!"

They led the horse on which the bewildered youth sat, close up to the walls. Leo Frangipane, in a voice like the blast of a trumpet: "Here, Petrus Leonis, is the Prefect of our city! Him and no other we want, we the Frangipani, and we speak for all the nobles of Rome!"

Three times his resounding voice made itself heard. But no reply came; everything remained perfectly still, as if the castle were under a spell or stricken with death. (However, it was only a massive fortress of amazing strength, encircled with a triple ring of walls, the like of which is not to be found in all Rome.)

Immediately afterwards Leo Frangipane ordered the castle to be attacked.

THE chronicle relates:

While they were trying to rush the gates with their iron clubs and battering-rams, and shooting their arrows over the walls (there was still no sign of movement within the castle), a procession was suddenly seen to emerge from a narrow street in the rear of the assailants: in front walked some Brothers of Mercy (it is they who carry the sick and the dead to their resting-places) followed by a number of priests all praying aloud; at the end came a group of women and young girls in the midst of whom was a bier, borne by some more Brothers of Mercy, on which lay stretched the body of Tullia Pier Leone, whether alive or dead one could not say, her mouth still wide open like a gaping wound in her face. They were making their way with the bier to the castle of Petrus Leonis.

As they found it impossible to proceed owing to the fray, the priests who accompanied the cortege stepped forward and called out in a loud voice above the tumult:

"Leo Frangipane, we command you in the name of the Holy Father to return home at once with your followers, for while you are seeking in this lawless fashion to impose a judge of life and death on our city, the judge sits already in judgment in your own house. A great tragedy has occurred: your father lies dead in his hall, but we are bearing Tullia Pier Leone to her house. Let us pass without delay, and pray with us for her life, that your brother Cencius may not be branded as her murderer!"

At these words, the men who had followed Leo Frangipane took fright. They said to each other: After such omens, little good can come out of the enterprise of this young man. Let us follow the priests and go to our dead master. That is the best thing we can do at the moment.

And forthwith they broke up and hurried away.

THE chronicle relates:

Not many utterances of Petrus Leonis have been handed down to us. Our records speak of the shrewd and scrupulous silence that he observed at all times, and also of his large expressive hands which did his talking for him as it were, and by means of which he accomplished many of the things that now speak of him. We can quote, however, the exact words of a statement wrung from him in the hour of his grief for his daughter Tullia, when with mouth open like a death-wound in her face, she lay stretched on her couch before him. He sat weeping beside her pillow, for he loved all his children tenderly.

During his vigil, Desiderius Bericisi, one of Donna Bona's brothers, came to see him; these were enemies of the Frangipani, and had decided to stand by their brother-in-law. In fact they were merely waiting for the moment when he should break out and avenge himself for the outrage done to him.

Petrus Leonis, through his tears, raising his large hands towards Bericisi, as though he were offering him two empty plates: "What is vengeance? How will it help this child of mine, if we kill a multitude of people and squander our money uselessly? The anger of the Holy Father will be aroused, and the whole city will be plunged into strife, and in the end we shall have gained nothing, but lost much!"

When he got outside, Bericisi said to Donna Bona (she was also weeping, but more for rage and shame, than for sorrow): "We are truly sorry for you, sister, for one can see that your husband comes of a race that has already had to endure numberless wrongs; he no longer knows what a man owes to himself."

THE chronicle relates:

Meanwhile the whole city was in a turmoil, all its streets humming like a shell placed close to the ear—the ear in this case being that of the Holy Father Paschal.

The people: They had camped from morning till evening before the Castle of Pier Leone, forming as it were a fourth wall round its three-fold ring; for word had gone round that Donna Bona was distributing alms this day, as well as food and drink, in order that the recipients might go and pray in the churches for Tullia's life.

These having had their fill, rushing to the Lateran: "Vengeance for Tullia, Holy Father, and let Petrus Leonis be Prefect of our city!"

The Frangipani: They likewise turned up in large numbers, armed to the teeth, this time with Gratianus of the isle of Lycaonia at their head, swaggering about on his charger, and trying to look like his late uncle Johannes, behind him his two sons Robertus and Reino together with the pale young Leo with the blond pennon, and following them the Frangipani of Gradellis and those of Septemsolia, and the various other branches of the family, all in full force, so that the whole court of the Lateran resounded with the neighing and prancing of their horses, hummed with the din and bustle of their retainers—indeed, one would have said that the leader of an armed host was encamped inside the palace instead of the priestly head of Christendom.

The whole crowd of them pressing forward: "Holy Father, Cencius acted boldly, like a man. We claim his right to be judged by his own knightly order, which acquits him! Down with Petrus Leonis! Hurrah for the son of the late Prefect!"

The Cardinals: Leaving their palaces and their country seats, these also made as fast as they could for the Lateran Palace, urging along the placid mules on which they were mounted, with fierce impatience.

"Holy Father, we conjure you to give a decision in this matter such as will prevent the standard of mortal enmity from being unfurled between your two chief families, and the city of St. Peter from being plunged into civil strife at a time when Holy Church is deprived of the sword of the Emperor!"

The Pier Leoni: Finally these also arrived, forming an even larger group than any of the others; the riders were clad in silver and gold (so the people said, on account of their shining armor and trumpets), at the head of them rode a herald bearing the device of a Lion Rampant.

At sight of them, the priests in the Lateran: "Now may all the Saints help us! It would need more than the wisdom of King Solomon to get us out of this pass! They will begin slaughtering each other under the very eyes of the Holy Father!"

The people, on their knees in tearful lamentation: "Aye, and us too! They will slay us as well! Peace and deliverance, Holy Father! Death and curses to the disturbers of the peace!"

Meanwhile the riders of the Pier Leoni entered the court in good order, and without any show of hostility to the Frangipani, who trembled with rage as they watched them go by; and when they passed the priests they lowered the points of their swords, for Petrus Leonis had accustomed his men to do this at all times. A moment later a herald was seen to advance, fully armed, though not as for battle, but as for parade, when great princes are due to arrive. Calmly but with lordly gesture he blew on his silver trumpet; and then with head uplifted, so that his voice might carry to the balcony of the palace, he made the following declaration:

"The illustrious Consul of the Romans, Petrus Leonis, solemnly renounces his claim to the prefecture. This he does to give peace to the city, but most of all for the sake of our Holy Father. To him also he leaves it to pronounce judgment upon Cencius Frangipane for the crime done to his daughter Tullia."

This done, the herald and the other riders of the Pier Leoni turned their horses round and rode away.

THE priests in the court of the Lateran: "Jesus Christ be praised, who has saved us!"

The people: "Petrus Leonis be praised, who gives us peace!"

The Frangipani: "Our good sword be praised; we will not lay it aside in a hurry!" Voicing their disappointment, as they rode home: "It would have been better for us if the sly fox had not renounced his claim, for by so doing he will win great credit with the Papal Curia, and we may be quite sure he will make his own conditions!"

THE chronicle relates:

We know, however, that at that time the majority of the Cardinals, including those who were most experienced and skillful in settling the disputes of the nobles, which are always a source of danger to the city, urged the Holy Father, in view of Petrus Leonis's magnanimous and judicious renunciation of the prefecture, to confirm the son of the late Prefect in the appointment, and at the same time to impress upon that young man, who was easy to influence, the advisability of treating

Cencius Frangipane with the utmost leniency, in order to bring the fierce
Frangipani to a calmer frame of mind. Later on, when the situation
became less acute, a way could easily be found of letting the nobles know
exactly what Holy Church thought regarding their unchristian hatred
for the origin of the Pier Leoni. (Here they were hinting at the further
elevation of the young Petrus, who had recently been sent as Papal legate
to France, where, according to report, he had already rendered important
services to the Holy See. We know however, that while he was there he
not only carried out the Holy Father's missions, but also entered into
secret negotiations with the King's Chancellor regarding the dissolution
of Germany's imperial power.)

The Holy Father to those who were urging him to deal leniently
with Cencius Frangipane: "Yes, let us all pray for Cencius, that is to say,
for the life of Tullia Pier Leone."

THE chronicle relates:

In the meanwhile, Tullia, contrary to all fears and expectations, had
risen from what had seemed to be her deathbed, the open wound of her
mouth now closed like a scar drawn painfully together in her face. (And
so it remained for the rest of her days.)

Accordingly the proceedings against Cencius Frangipane were
dropped.

HERE is the letter relating thereto that we found in the chancery of the
Cardinal-Bishop Petrus of Portus. We have reason for thinking that it
was written by the Holy Father himself.

"...But because Christ has chosen to have mercy on you, Cencius
Frangipane, in that by delivering Tullia Pier Leone from death, He has
saved you from being her murderer, we also will have mercy on you, and
will allow you to go unpunished. Go then and show to your brothers
the mercy you have found in us. But know that among these there is no
other origin than the origin from Him in whose Name we are all equally
baptized, which origin signifies also the future of us all, namely the new

humanity or the mystical body of Jesus Christ, our King, in whom all the nations of the earth shall be united."

This letter was sent to the monastery of Sancta Maria Nova to be read aloud to Cencius Frangipane, who had been placed in confinement there.

But at that hour, Leo Frangipane was as usual keeping his brother company, and playing to him on his lute the theme of the *ezzelina*, which Cencius insisted on hearing every day; he seemed to draw such strength and comfort therefrom that it might have been the air of some heroic lay commemorating a good deed for which he was being unjustly persecuted.

When the Cardinal-Bishop of Portus, who brought the letter, heard the strains of the *ezzelina*—the brothers were leaping and running with sounding step along the stately corridors of the whole monastery, like two young savages—he was so horrified that his feet refused to function and he almost collapsed outside the door.

Whereupon the Prior of the monastery, who accompanied him, told him that these same strains were to be heard every single day; which, in his view, clearly pointed to the fact that Cencius Frangipane had no consciousness whatever of his guilt.

The Cardinal-Bishop: "Truly, God has here exercised an even greater mercy than we knew!" (By which he meant that it is hard to condemn a man who does not feel himself guilty.)

They then entered and read the letter aloud.

The two young Frangipani: At first they remained silent, and gazed with a look of naive surprise on their young faces into the faces of the two ecclesiastics. Then shaking their heads, so that the pennons of their blond hair hung deep over their foreheads, they said in a mild voice: "You priests have strange dreams!"

Nevertheless the Cardinal-Bishop believed that the letter had touched their hearts and said he was willing to give them his blessing.

They knelt down like dutiful children, but with the same look of candid wonderment still on their faces; then all of a sudden they jumped up from their knees with a violent start, crying out: "Go on dreaming, you priests! We will wake you up sooner than you think!"

From that day forth Cencius and Leo Frangipane declared: "It is only now that we perceive the real chasm. The Pope is become a stranger among us; he does not want to be Bishop of the Romans, he wants to be Bishop of the whole universe, folding all peoples in his embrace, not, however, with iron arms, as sovereign of the world, like our mighty Rome of old, but as a mother, for whom they are all equal—the Seat of the Universe is to be fixed henceforth in heaven!"

The young Tusculans: "Oh, you wild, unruly Frangipani, what children you are, not to have perceived this until now!"

The chronicle relates:

Meanwhile the news of the threats uttered by the two Frangipani had reached the Lateran Palace, and the frightened Cardinals strongly urged upon the Holy Father that it would be better to give up the idea of raising the young Petrus Pier Leonis to the cardinalate, so as to avoid irritating the family of the Frangipani still further. Moreover the latter would be taught a lesson and be made to realize their injustice, if they saw that Petrus Leonis demanded no reward for his loyal services; the fact would be self-evident, and not even they would be able to dispute it. (It was just about this time that the young Petrus returned from France.)

We now give the secret history of the elevation of the young Petrus Pier Leonis to the purple.

(From the notes of the Cardinal-Bishop Petrus of Portus.)

...Since then I have often raised my hands in prayer, that it might be granted to me before I die to behold once again the light of supernatural charity shining in the countenance of the Holy Father, as I beheld it in the Castle of Trebico in the presence of King Henry; in order that this vision might be a consoling witness to me in my last hour, of the charity of the King of Heaven. Jesus Christ be praised, who has heard my prayer! For I verily believe that it has been the same with the purple of this young Cardinal as it was with the blessing of King Henry, namely that the bestowing of it has been a question put to a human soul, and one which will follow him to the end of his days.

This is what I saw and heard when I was telling our Holy Father about the threats of the two Frangipani, of which I myself was witness.

The young Petrus Leonis entered the room just after the Holy Father had been discussing with me the question of his elevation to the purple. But as I was of the same opinion as my brother Cardinals, the Holy Father had decided to give up the idea of his nomination for the present.

We had not seen the young Petrus since his return from France. Our Holy Father embraced him like a son, for his deepest sympathy went out to him on account of the wrong done to his sister Tullia, and because of all the evil things that the captains were saying about his father.

The young Petrus kneeling down: "Holy Father, you know that my family left it to you to pass judgment on Cencius Frangipane?"

The Holy Father: "Yes, my son, we know that your father has now great glory in the eyes of Christ."

The young Petrus: "But who will efface in the eyes of the world the affront put upon us?"

The Holy Father (very gently): "My son, do you feel aggrieved, because the Lord Himself has been pleased to pardon your enemy Cencius Frangipane?"

The young Petrus, suddenly raising his hands as in an access of passion (he had large, busy hands like his father, but they were not so reticent as the latter's, and at that moment they struck one as impetuous to the point of violence): "Holy Father, we have kept the commandments of Holy Church in every detail. We have fought for you since the days of our Holy Father Gregory; none of your Roman families has stood by you so loyally as we! Our house has been your house, our power has been your power, our money has been at the disposal of your friends—"

The Holy Father (recoiling a step, but with the same gentleness as before): "You are taking many words of thanks out of our mouth, Petrus Pier Leonis."

But the young Petrus went on, like a torrent overflowing its banks: "And I too, Holy Father, I too, fought for you to the best of my feeble strength the whole time of your struggle with the Salian, when everyone was denying you the justice due to you!"

The Holy Father (with the same tender and peaceful expression on his face as on the day when the Great Synod in the Lateran questioned him in regard to King Henry): "We thank you, my son; but can you be sure that justice for ourself was any part of our care at that time?" (This is the only occasion on which I heard our Holy Father refer to that day; but so dearly did he cherish the soul of this young man, that he was even willing to yield up to him the great secret of his own particular sacrifice.)

The young Petrus, still carried away by his feelings: "And yet, Holy Father, I beg and implore you, not for my sake, nor for the sake of my family, but I beg of you—God is my witness—for the sake of Holy Church herself, to see that she does not incur the reproach of having failed to see justice done."

The Holy Father (in a low but firm voice): "My son, justice exists only in hell; in heaven there is grace, and on earth there is the cross. But the Church is here, that she may bless those who bear this cross. And therefore we bless you and yours, Petrus Pier Leonis: you also bear the cross of Jesus Christ."

At those words the young Petrus gave a start; his whole body became strangely contorted as if he were suffering agonies of pain, and there was a note almost of horror in his voice as he blurted: "The Cross of Christ—that's our reward?"

Then I saw our Holy Father turn pale as though an abyss were opening before his soul. A moment later he extended both his arms to the kneeling Petrus and said, his countenance engraven as it were with the imprint of the divine mercy: "My son, if it is a question of your soul, I will transform the cross in such a way that you will be able to bear it lovingly: know that the purple of the Church which you so eagerly desire, is the purple of Christ in the presence of Pontius Pilate! It will be your privilege to wear it in the future."

The young Petrus then withdrew in confusion.

But I kneeling down before our Holy Father, said to him in a loud voice: "Holy Father, now I know that the Church of Christ is not of this world, for here we are steering between Pagans and Jews and no one is capable of understanding the course we follow."

The Holy Father: "Yes, my brother, it is for the sake of both of these that Christ died."

To which I, through my tears: "And you, Holy Father, I am afraid they will kill you too!"

The Holy Father: "It is better that they should kill us than that a soul should be damned."

He then commanded me to keep silence about everything I had just heard.

Not long afterwards the young Petrus Pier Leonis was nominated Cardinal Deacon of Sancta Maria in Transtiberion. And from that day the Frangipani really did say quite openly: "The Pope must be killed."

THE fathers of the Tusculans.

At that time these took counsel with Stephanus Normannus: "Our young men are still living in the days of Crescentius and of the Dux Alberic, our great ancestors who made and unmade Popes at their own good pleasure. But those days are now past. The Pope has regained his prestige in all the countries of Christendom, and it is through him that Rome still has dominion over the whole earth. Are we going to deprive our city of its last glory by allowing him to be driven out? But this is what will happen if we let these senseless Frangipani have their way. We sent them against Petrus Leonis, but not against the Holy Father."

They then decided that one of the Tusculans should offer his daughter in marriage to Cencius, and that the other should offer his to the young Leo; they hoped in this way to tame the savage hearts of the two young men, and at the same time to acquire a paternal authority over them.

The young Frangipani to the Counts of Tusculum: "Our hearts are grown old with grief, and women no longer interest us; henceforth we will seek consolation from none save from her who is the queen of all women!" (They were still young enough to talk in this fashion! But by the "queen of all women" we understood them to mean the Mother of God.)

CONCERNING the queen of all women of the two Frangipani.

There is a day in the year when we sing the hymn, "*Nobilibus fueras.*" We then fetch the holy image from the chapel of the Lateran Palace, and carry it in procession at night to the ancient Forum of the Romans. There we wash its feet in an old fountain with great fervor, chanting hymns the while; in olden times our Pagan ancestors used to wash their holy images in the same place.

We then proceed with the holy image to Sancta Maria, in order that Our Savior may behold His sorrowful Mother again. By this time most of our torches have burnt out, and many in the procession are walking by the bare light of the moon. In the end we all walk by the bare light of the moon. (But it is not the moon alone, it is also the past splendor of the things we walk among, of the things, namely, that have no end.)

We then wind round the Palatine hill, past the Septemsolia Palace and the Coliseum until we reach the ruined temple, known as the Temple of the goddess Rome. Here lie a number of tall light-blue columns, all broken and tumbled about pell-mell, as if the centuries had played skittles with them. But suddenly they shoot up erect again, and stand there, as if from out its heap of ruins this temple were raising its own immortal face to view once more.

At this stage of our way we intone the prayer: "*Sancta Maria, ora pro Roma!*" But the two Frangipani chant: "*Sancta Roma, ora pro nobis!*"

We heard them pray thus many times, but never with such fervor as at the death of our Holy Father Paschal, before they burst in upon the conclave in Sancta Maria in Palara.

THE conclave in Sancta Maria in Palara.

In the basilica of St. Peter there is an hour (it occurs under the pontificate of every Pope, once, twice, or three times) when all light suddenly departs from the candles and lamps that burn there, and everything is dark, as though the night of death rose from the tomb of the holy apostle Peter who sleeps under this church, and enveloped the whole place, thence projecting its shadow far beyond over the city. It happened thus at the coronation of King Henry; we ourselves experienced this night as we sat talking to the woman Susa in the ancient Forum of the Romans.

But during the election of our Holy Father Gelasius (he had been at all times a loyal servant of our Holy Father Paschal) we beheld not only that darkness, but flashes of lightning as well; thunder was heard and the raging of the elements, and afterwards there was a torrential downpour of rain. From this, the impious among us concluded that the "night" we had experienced had not been what we call "the night of St. Peter," but a perfectly natural night proceeding from a violent storm, which, as they pointed out, left traces of itself in large pools of water and wringing-wet clothes for many days afterwards. Those who spoke thus were clearly proved wrong, however, by what happened in the course of this storm.

For we are frankly of opinion that the two Frangipani, like the veritable instruments of Satan himself, burst into the conclave of the Holy Father Gelasius. Not only the women, but even the little children, shrieked with terror, as they careered over the Forum shouting like the four riders of hell, whom we had heard after the black coronation of the Salian: "Ho! ho! Woe to the Pope! We are going to seize him, or rather the pretender who calls himself Pope, the false Bishop of Rome, the foreigner! We, we will appoint the true Bishop, he shall be Pope of the Romans and naught else!"

Then battering the doors of Sancta Maria in Palara with heavy clubs, they crashed through the falling framework and drowned with their trumpets the *Te Deum* which had already been intoned in honor of the elected Pontiff.

Many of us rushed off at once to the woman Susa, weeping and wailing: "Mother Susa, the horsemen of Antichrist have broken in, and their name is Cencius and Leo Frangipane!"

Meanwhile people were flocking together from all sides: the young

Prefect of the city with his men, Petrus Leonis with his, Stephanus
Normannus with his, the two Tusculans with their sons, the Bericisi,
and at their heels the city mob in wild tumult as in the days of the
Salian. Pouring over the ruins of the Forum they all made for the Castle
of the Frangipani where the Holy Father and the Cardinals were held
prisoners.

The woman Susa (today she was not in Sancta Maria de Inferno,
but was seated in front of her little broken-down house, which is known
as the "House of the Vestals"), with hands clasped irresolutely, like a
woman who is uncertain what she ought to pray for; we had never seen
her look so cross: "You make a great mistake if you think that Antichrist
will arrive with sounding trumpets and snorting steeds; he will come as
a polished active man of the world, who knows how to bide his time, like
all clever people."

In the meantime they had succeeded in getting the Holy Father
away from the Castle of the Frangipani. Petrus Leonis held with his
own hand the bridle of a white mule on which the Pope had been raised;
and thus mounted he was brought back amid shouts of jubilation to the
Lateran.

The woman Susa, suddenly getting up, with the same abruptness
as when the lout had questioned her, and looking crosser than ever: "I
refuse to say any more!" Now it was just about this time that we began to
hear it said in various quarters that she was secretly a heretic, like those
of whom there are now so many in our Lombard cities. (We knew perfectly well, however, that this was mere gossip spread by the same great
lout to whom on that previous occasion we had given the answer he so
richly deserved; for this he can never forgive her.)

We, catching hold of her by the ends of her black cloak: "Mother
Susa, you were quite right when you refused to answer that other time,
but us you may safely confide in!"

She: "I refuse to say any more—I mean it, so please let me go! I am
a poor ignorant woman, who is not worth listening to!"

She then entered her tiny dwelling and bolted the door.

THE Tusculans that same evening:

"Truly, these two Frangipani are a great piece of luck for Petrus Leonis; they have succeeded in forcing us all to take his part and to fight at his side!"

The next morning the Frangipani made a surprise attack on the Holy Father while he was saying Mass in Saint Praxedis. After this the Cardinal Pier Leone published a letter from the Chancellor of France, and we all implored him on our knees to arrange for the Pope to take refuge in that country.

We never saw the Holy Father Gelasius again, we only saw his successor, the great French Pope Callixtus, who was chosen in the monastery of Cluny. This Pope, aided by the swords of French knights, demolished the castles of the Frangipani. Thus was verified the sentence of the *Gesta Dei per Francos*.

VII

Fʀᴏᴍ the archives of our golden City of Rome: We have witnessed
many triumphal entries into our city, some with swords and some without swords, some with laurels and some without laurels, some of kings
and some of emperors, and we have witnessed in addition many grand
processions of our Popes, but never have we beheld anything to equal in
magnificence the entry into our city of our new Sovereign Pontiff from
France. It is true that at first there were people among us who murmured,
because the newly-elected Pope was a foreigner and his election had
not taken place in our city of Rome. These were heard to say: "Certainly
Cluny is a famous place and a very holy monastery, but nevertheless
Popes ought not to be elected there; our Sovereign Pontiff must be chosen and installed in Rome first of all, otherwise we will not hang out our
garlands and banners, nor will we hold ourselves bound to obey him."
Accordingly until the last moment before our Sovereign Pontiff made his
entry, anyone looking down our streets would have seen a large number
of houses whose facades still remained obstinately bare of all decoration.

Then suddenly all was bustle and excitement; an army of huge
creaking wagons descended upon us, laden with costly carpets, scarlet
draperies, and gold embroideries such as are worked in Arabia and at
Byzantium, and with men marching beside them, shouting at the top
of their voices: "These costly carpets and stuffs are for those who are
willing to hang them out for the reception of the Holy Father Callixtus

II! Those who have not yet bound their garlands, let them set about it
at once, for prizes will be given for the best decorated houses in our
city. They can be called for at the palace of the illustrious Consul Petrus
Leonis!"

Within a few moments, all the houses whose bare walls had so sulk-
ily defied our rejoicings, seemed suddenly to have turned red with shame,
so much scarlet drapery was to be seen hanging out of their windows to
hide their nakedness. Soon our whole city resembled the purple throne
of a King, and not a single old column that still stood erect on its marble
feet, but had begun to bloom like a young rose tree.

Meanwhile our Sovereign Pontiff from France had crossed the gar-
landed threshold of our city: a fine-looking man of princely bearing,
seated on a white palfrey, and crowned magnificently with the tiara,
beneath which his keen intelligent face had the air of a falcon eyeing its
surroundings from under the gable of a tower. One glance at him was
enough to make us realize that there must be no delay or hesitation on
our part in recognizing this man, and that there could be no question of
making him submit to a second election in Rome. Clearly he already had
all Holy Church behind him, and it was we who were dangerously near
the point of putting ourselves outside the pale. Accordingly we speed-
ily arrived at the same unanimity as our scarlet-bedraped houses, and
shouted: "Long life and honor to our Holy Father Callixtus! Praise and
thanks to the land of France and the great monastery of Cluny, where St.
Peter chose him for his successor!"

But there happened to be with us a man who enjoyed some reputation as a wit, and he promptly remarked that the famous phrase about
the *Gesta Dei per Francos* ought to be changed to *Gesta Dei per Petrum
Leonis*, since but for the political foresight of the Cardinal Petrus, the
land of France would hardly have had the honor of giving asylum to
the Holy Father Gelasius in his need, of humiliating his enemies at the
present time, and of providing the orphaned Church with such a mighty
successor. But in Rome no one had worked so energetically for this last
as Petrus Leonis.

At this a voice was heard above the crowd in reply: "Far better *Gesta Dei per Petrum Leonis* than *Gesta Dei per Francos*! Romans! We have rid ourselves of the Germans! Are you now going to suffer our great Pontiffs to settle an army of French knights among us?"

FROM the archives of our golden city of Rome.

About this time the first emissaries of the Lombards set up their pulpits among us, addressing us thus wise: "A new tree is now flourishing in our cities which, unlike all the trees that have hitherto raised their proud branches to heaven, was not planted by the hands of our great lords of noble lineage, but by the hands of the industrious burghers and the toiling people. If you knew what a precious and glorious thing is the freedom of our cities, you would hasten to plant a similar tree in your own city—which truly is worthy of such! Then you would no longer have to submit to being devoured by your captains and bled white by the peoples of other lands!"

THE chronicle relates:

In those days the two Tusculans took counsel with Stephanus Normannus, and this was the burden of their deliberations:

"We must adopt a new outlook, or rather we must return to the old one which ever characterized our city of Rome in the days of its glory; otherwise we shall never get the French knights to return home or the people to remain quiet. The enterprise of these Frangipani was not Roman, it was just a tumult of barbarians, of those barbarians in fact whose blood already flows half-submerged and stifled in their veins, or it would not have felt the need of rising and vaunting itself in this way. But our family descends in a pure line from the Anici, and for us, *Roman* means this: that it is not blood but spirit which constitutes the most solid wall of defence. Our grammarians still point to the place on the Capitol where once the statues of all the peoples of the earth stood assembled, each wearing round its neck a little bell which started ringing as soon as any danger threatened Rome from its land. Contrary to the foolish opinion of the multitude, this contrivance owed nothing to the magic arts of the magician Virgil (although Virgil was undoubtedly a great magician), but was devised by the loyalty of those same peoples; in other words, because their sons were recognized as citizens of our city, and felt at home within our walls, they made common cause with us in all our affairs."

Then they said to their sons: "Go on crowning the idol you have set up, if you want to; you can extinguish your torches before it, or spread your carpets over it as much as you like, but understand that for the future Petrus Leonis is no longer to be called "he" but by his right name. We have no just cause of complaint against him. We all strive for power, every one of us; and we cannot fairly resent in him what we are equally guilty of ourselves."

AFTERWARDS they saddled their horses and rode to the palace of Petrus Leonis. Stephanus Normannus, who was the cleverest of the three, acted as spokesman, and made the following speech:

"Well, Petrus Leonis, we know that you are a sensible man who does not allow his passions and resentments to override his judgment, but views things in their proper perspective, and will therefore be guided at the present juncture by a just consideration of what the situation in which we are all of us now placed, demands of us. We for our part are anxious to ensure that our Sovereign Pontiff shall remain in Rome and enjoy tranquil rule in the future. If then you are willing, we are ready to bury the past and join with you in a common endeavor to achieve this end. Let us make a pact to work together for the peace of our city and for the defence and security of the Holy See; in this way we shall revive the ancient glory of Rome and prove to the world that we are quite capable of protecting our Popes without the help of foreigners."

In answer Petrus Leonis held out his big, honest hand.

Stephanus Normannus outside the door, wiping the sweat from his brow, for he had found it hard to make this speech calmly though he had delivered it: "Has our visit, do you think, been a triumph for Petrus Leonis or a humiliation?"

Whereupon one of the Counts: "For us it would have been a humiliation to hold out our hands to one of our enemies, but for him it was certainly a triumph that we had to offer him ours."

And so Petrus Leonis rose higher and higher; he rose through honor and he rose through dishonor, he rose through friendship and he rose through enmity, he rose through good report and he rose through evil report; there was nothing through which he did not rise, but just as the groats and pennies changed unceasingly into gold bezants in his hands, so did everything that happened to him ultimately transform itself into a triumph.

But of this final triumph of Petrus Leonis over the family of the Frangipani we say: it was won not over that family alone, but over the whole nobility of our city.

FROM the archives of our golden city of Rome.

Meanwhile the fact that Cardinal Pier Leone, who had always defended the thesis of the *Gesta Dei per Francos*, had actually returned with this French Pope and overthrown the fierce Frangipani, and that the Holy Father could again dwell among us, gave us a great deal to think about. At that time we firmly believed that this French Pope was going to transfer the empire to France, and that, with a new devout emperor on the throne, the danger of Antichrist would be averted from Holy Church and we should all by the grace of God be once again preserved from him. This was such a comforting thought that for the time being we actually forgot all about our prophetess, the woman Susa. We were strengthened in our hopes by what some of the retainers of the French barons told us. They related that while the Holy Father Callixtus was on his way to Rome, the stars at night were seen in many places of the land of France to move towards each other in such a way that they formed a crown, which was immediately recognized as the crown of Constantine. Furthermore the great bell of the Cathedral of Notre Dame in Paris was heard to peal of its own accord in tones so like the imperial bell at Speyer, that the Germans who dwelt in the city all swore that they had

heard the latter. But as regards the imperial bell at Speyer, people from
Germany have told us that since the black coronation, the united efforts
of ten men have not been able to set it in motion and make it peal.

HOWEVER, while this story was circulating among us, our new Sovereign Pontiff had arranged through the Cardinal Legate Lambert of Ostia
for a scepter to be forwarded to Worms on the Rhine, in order that King
Henry might confirm the German bishops in their fiefs. King Henry
on his side handed back to the Legate the rings and staffs of the German bishops, by this gesture abdicating once more the Investiture which
he had previously wrung from the Holy Father Paschal; this was afterwards known as the Concordat of Worms, or the great Peace between
the Church and the Empire. And so we in Rome had suddenly to ring all
our bells for the victory of Holy Church, and also for the Empire of the
Germans; for, according to us, on this day the black coronation became
white again, and King Henry Emperor of us all. When, however, the
Holy Father was told how the people had mistakenly regarded him as a
French Pope, he shook his head, as one does at the relating of old wives'
tales. Then with a smile on his mobile and intelligent features: "There are
no French Popes, there are only Popes of the Church of Christ."

WE paid a visit to the woman Susa.

Again we found her not in Sancta Maria, but in her little house,
seated at her hearth, whereon a thick broth was simmering. She herself
was scraping carrots, with the busy air of a person who wants to avoid
looking up.

We (a little embarrassed at having neglected her so long): "Well,
mother Susa, you will not turn us away today as you did last time!" In
truth, we expected to find her jubilant because the Empire was remain-
ing with Germany, for that had been her wish all along.

She (but not quite with the joy we had expected): "Yes, Jesus Christ
be praised, the rightful order among the nations has been preserved."

We: "And Antichrist, it seems, has become merely a children's bogey."

All of a sudden she burst into tears. Sobbing into her hands: "Oh, Emperor Henry, why do you come so late? I see an open grave in the Cathedral of Speyer!"

We, frightened to death: "And what do you see of Antichrist?"

She, still more bitterly: "That Christians are guilty of him, that is what I see! I see the Emperor Henry guilty of Antichrist! I see the Cross of Christ set up in the city of Rome!"

We: "Now you are speaking in riddles, we do not in the least understand what you mean!"

Suddenly she sprang to her feet; a look of wild consternation came over her face, such as we had never yet seen in her: "Let me be! Why will you not leave me in peace? Go away! I have told you already that no one ought to believe me! Don't you see how wretched I am?"

We then took the liberty of warning her—very respectfully of course—that she must be careful not to do or say anything which might prejudice her good name. As a matter of fact we knew that from time to time exalted persons among the clergy sent their agents to visit her; and this caused us some misgiving, for we did not know whether they did this, because, like ourselves, they honored her and wished to hear her revelations, or whether it was because they regarded her with suspicion owing to the report spread about her by that mischief-making lout, whom may God punish therefor.

And so we said to her very earnestly: "Mother Susa, it would be a bitter grief to us if a single person were to take you for the kind of woman we know you are not!"

She, holding her hands to her head: "But perhaps I am! Yes, would to God I were one of those whom the Devil has led astray!"

At that moment, we saw to our horror that one of the persons of whom we had been thinking had slipped in with us unobserved. He kept in the background, a young man of elegant appearance, dressed like a person of good standing; we noticed at once that he had a clerical look about him; moreover the knots of his headgear had been carelessly tied, so that we could see the round tonsure between them.

We hastily turned to him: "Good sir, you hear that Mother Susa does not wish to see anybody today. Let us go then, and not worry her further." So saying we took a hurried departure, leaving him no choice but to accompany us.

He, while we were crossing the Forum: he had observed that we frequently visited the woman Susa; perhaps then we could tell him what she meant by saying she wished that the Devil tempted her?

We told him the precise truth: She is thinking of the coming of Antichrist, which she sees before her eyes. This causes her such anguish of soul, that she would rather her vision turned out to be a deception of the Devil than that it should prove true, so dear to her are Christ and His Holy Church.

He then took his leave of us. Some of us, however, followed him without his knowing it, and sure enough he disappeared behind the *Curia Julia* into the massive building occupied by the *Canonici* of Saint Adrianus. So we knew where we were.

THE chronicle relates:

It was during the pontificate of Pope Callixtus that we first heard it suggested that the Cardinal Pier Leone would one day be Pope. The people were heard to reason thus: We now have a strong and energetic Sovereign Pontiff on the throne of St. Peter, and it is to our benefit, for he preserves peace in our city of Rome. Should we be fortunate enough also to have a rich Pope given us in the future, it would be a just and happy consummation after all the sad, distressful war-years that lie behind us. Even among the clergy there were those who said: The world is now become a hard nut, and it is not possible to crack it only with the love of Christ. The people are right: we see today what a strong Pope can do, may God provide us with another such in the future, so that we may never again have to endure what we went through in the evil days of the Frangipani.

Meanwhile the huge castle of these latter, near Sancta Maria Nova, still lay demolished; fragments of its red and brown masonry could be seen scattered about among the white ruins of the Forum—one might almost say "splashed about," for they looked like the spars of a wrecked ship among the foam-flakes of a stormy sea, out of which rose like a black reef the single charred tower where the living quarters lie, this being the only part of the structure that still stood erect. In this ruin, brooding in sulky retirement, dwelt the two Frangipani with their cousin Jacoba.

Day and night Jacoba pleaded with her cousins to set about rebuilding the castle, now that the French knights had departed. But the Frangipani had not the money for building, like their father Johannes, to whom Petrus Leonis had advanced it. Nor was there anyone in the days of Pope Callixtus who would have come to their aid; even their own cousins of Septemsolia and Gradellus remained as if dead behind their towers and their walls. Jacoba might just as well have urged the deaf ruins of the castle itself to raise themselves up, so great was the dejection and helplessness of the two Frangipani. Jacoba, however, was secretly glad, for she believed that her own hour had come.

JACOBA Frangipane.

She still adorned her long slender hands with sparkling rings and bracelets, but her poor ugly face had lost its frightened, pathetic look, for she now knew that her cousin Cencius would never caress her beautiful hands. Nor did she desire any longer that he should; for when the heart of a woman is rebuffed too often, it ends by turning away of itself. And so her precious jewels jingled on her wrists like dead glass when she saluted her young cousins with outstretched hand in the Roman fashion. She held to the pact more passionately even than the young men (as is the wont of women who have silenced their hearts), and now that the two Tusculans had been detached by their fathers, she and her two cousins were left to carry it on practically alone. But, as we all know, in matters where men employ force, women use cunning.

JACOBA Frangipane and her cousins.

Jacoba: "You once said to your father: 'Here serpents are no use, we need swords.' It is now time to say the exact opposite. In Rome no one can now accomplish anything without Petrus Leonis, not even overthrow him; you must endeavor to beat him with his own weapons."

The two Frangipani: "We want to beat him with ours, for were we to beat him with his, he would have conquered us, not we him."

They then drew their swords and pointed them against their breasts, exclaiming that they would rather go to hell with them than to heaven with a serpent.

Jacoba: "Very well then, you look after your little hell-horses, my pretty cousins; in the meantime I will rear a couple of serpents for you. It may easily happen that thanks to them your horses may be able to take the bit between the teeth."

JACOBA and her cousins.

Jacoba: "What will you say, my pretty cousins, if I sell my beautiful rings? Will you rebuild your castle and renew the fight for Rome?"

The young Leo (he often wept his heart out to her as to a devoted aunt, for it was as such that she acted towards him at that time): "You must not do that, Jacoba, for these rings suit you wonderfully well. There are people who say that your hands are worthy of the old statues that our grammarians rave about. We ourselves do not understand much about these things, but we should not like it to be said that we were barbarians who despoiled your hands of their beauty."

Jacoba Frangipane: "What need have I of beautiful things for my hands? I am ugly and faded, but Rome is eternal."

Cencius, awkwardly (for he did not deem it possible that a woman could set her heart on Rome, but thought she wished to sacrifice her rings for his sake): "No one will give you a price for them that would be any use to us. The only person that could do so in these hard times is Petrus Leonis himself. But you can hardly expect him to come to our aid after all that has passed between us. So keep your rings. Besides, they are beautiful, whereas money"—contemptuously—"is filthy and stupid."

Jacoba quietly: "The money of Petrus Leonis is clever!"

FROM the archives of our golden city of Rome.

All this while we had often wondered why Tullia Pier Leone had not entered one of our convents; for there she would have found—at least that was our opinion—a happy retreat, a place of consolation after all that had befallen her. But Petrus Leonis had other views in regard to his daughter.

In fact it was now that we learned that Count Roger of Sicily had asked her hand in marriage (he is the great Norman prince, of whom rumor says that he aspires to the title of King. Hence our wits have suggested that it will be for the King of Rome to gild the crown of the King of Sicily). Hereafter we saw Donna Bona looking radiant; she might have been the bride herself, so delighted was she that her husband's daughter who had previously been the victim of such an outrage, was now to be the wife of a reigning prince. In Tullia herself, however, we beheld no such radiance, save in her wealth of precious stones; for Donna Bona had directed that all the little gold and silver bells of her dress should be covered with jewels, so that the whole of Rome could hardly provide all the pearls and precious stones that were needed for this wedding.

FROM the archives of our golden city of Rome.

Now we do not believe that Petrus Leonis really needed Jacoba's jewels, but we believe this: it has often been said in his praise that he brought from his old religion to his new the most scrupulous observance of all precepts and laws, so that we are quite ready to credit him in this case with wishing to perform a good action towards his enemies, as Holy Church prescribes that we should. At the same time there are some people for whom well-doing and self-interest happen to mean the same thing. (We ourselves have always aspired to be of their number, for they seem to have found the best solution to our earthly problems.) In hinting at this, however, we are not now thinking of the evil that was spoken of Petrus Leonis at a later date, all we mean is that he was very anxious at that time to get rid of his enemies without drawing the sword, and that it was precisely then that he purchased Jacoba Frangipane's rings.

JACOBA Frangipane's rings.

The chronicle relates:

Of Tullia Pier Leone the servants of the palace say: "In the old days we always found her sweet and gentle, but latterly it has sometimes seemed as if the painful wound of her mouth were suppurating, so much bitterness issues therefrom. But whenever this happens Tullia immediately starts crying."

When Jacoba Frangipane entered the large hall of the palace—all the Pier Leone family were sitting there in state, looking very grand and opulent in their expensive chairs: Donna Bona in her silks, the Cardinal in his purple, and Prince Roger of Sicily next to his bride—Tullia's bluish-pale face turned crimson to the roots of her slate-colored hair, for her mind went back to the occasion when she had last seen Jacoba, to the night, namely, when they had danced the *ezzelina* at the Frangipani's. It is said that she did not rise to greet Jacoba owing to the weight of her bejeweled bells; some maintain, however, that she remained seated on purpose. Accordingly, as Jacoba stepped painfully forward, she had nothing to encourage her but the twitching wound in Tullia's face.

Tullia Pier Leone: her first impulse was to put her arms round her betrothed, but she held back, for the fear suddenly came upon her that he might inadvertently start dancing with her, so she merely felt for his hand.

To Jacoba Frangipane: "Jacoba, this is my future husband. And meanwhile who has become yours?" (She knew quite well that Jacoba had loved in vain her own former fiancé.)

Jacoba to herself, like her young cousins: "Rome! Rome!" In this way she succeeded in trampling herself under foot, so to speak.

Humbly to Tullia Pier Leone: "Why do you ask me, Tullia Pier Leone? I am ugly and withered, and must offer my rings and armlets for sale, in order that we may live. Please put in a good word with your father."

Tullia: "There is no need to persuade my father, for it is a small matter with him to buy what gives us pleasure. Show us what you have brought!"

While she was showing her treasures, Jacoba could not but think of the day when, at her uncle's command, she had offered her hand with her ring to the young Petrus Pier Leonis, and she began to tremble, as on that occasion, so bitter was the memory to her pride.

Again she made an inward ejaculation: "Rome, Rome, help me to bear it!"

Meanwhile Tullia cast such a cold, contemptuous glance on the rings that the blood mounted to Jacoba's cheeks.

Tullia: "You cannot expect much for these rings, my poor Jacoba!" And as she said this she began to cry.

Suddenly the Cardinal to himself: "We are haughty, why is it we find it so hard to behold the humiliated? We are ambitious, why can we not bear to see those whom we trample on? Can it be that we love our enemies?" Aloud to Jacoba: "Damsel, the bishoprics in the Campania are still as impoverished as ever; what are these rings worth to you?" (But it was to Jacoba as if he had said: "Your hands are still as beautiful as ever," so consoling was the chivalrous tone of his voice.)

At the same time she felt strangely glad that he had previously repulsed her beautiful hand.

Looking straight into his intelligent, ambitious face: "They are worth to me as much as the friendship of my two cousins, but that is worth to me as much as the castle by Sancta Maria Nova, when it still stood erect."

At this the Prince of Sicily gave a hearty laugh: "Truly, damsel, you know how to bargain with jewels! Why not say, while you are about it: they are worth as much as the Holy Father's crown?"

The Cardinal with some annoyance: "We are not concerned here with the crown of the Holy Father, but we were speaking just now of the crown of Sicily."

Petrus Leonis, however, who had remained silent the whole time, now stood up, and with his large busy hands carried Jacoba's jewels into the room where stood the fine gold scales on which are weighed all the moneys and jewels that flow to his house from all parts of the world. But Jacoba's rings and bracelets were not weighed on these scales, but they were weighed with the words: the friendship of the Frangipane family.

Petrus Leonis to Jacoba: "Here is your price for the rings, damsel, but if you need more, come again; it ill beseems a Consul and Senator of the Romans to suffer you and your kin to be housed in a ruin."

THE two Frangipani and their cousin Jacoba.

The two Frangipani: "Where did you find all these coins, Jacoba?" (Petrus Leonis had paid his money in old Roman coins, which are of a finer and heavier gold than ours. Consequently the two Frangipani thought that Jacoba had unearthed a treasure in some cave or garden, for such things often happen in our city of Rome if one of us is in luck's way.)

Jacoba: "I am not going to tell you where I found these coins."

The two Frangipani: "Are there any more then, as you make such a mystery about it?"

She: "There are plenty more in the place where these come from, so get on with your building!"

At this the two Frangipani remained dead silent for a moment. Then they suddenly threw their swords straight up in the air so that they sprang back into their arms like flashes of blue lightning. The two Frangipani: "Rome! Rome! So thou thyself hast willed to help us!" Then: "May thy gods now grant that Pope Callixtus may die!"

Jacoba Frangipane: "Maybe he will, my pretty cousins: my serpents are ready."

Not long after this the rumor circulated that the Cardinal Pier Leone was aiming at the Papal crown, as his father was spending money profusely in order to buy him friends. Whereupon the Cardinals remarked to each other: "Unless this rumor is stopped, our brother Pier Leone will never become Pope, for the suspicion of simony presses heavily upon him."

And so begins the second conflict of the Frangipane family; and of it we say that it was fought not with swords, but with serpents.

VIII

EXTRACT from the notes of the Cardinal-Bishop Petrus of Portus:

As I am writing for those who will live after us and be unaware of many things that are now matters of common knowledge, I will here mention that our Sovereign Pontiff, the Holy Father Callixtus II, was, before his election to the Papal throne, none other than the Archbishop Guy of Vienne, who had excommunicated King Henry with Bell, Book and Candle, and been the most bitter of all in his opposition to our Holy Father Paschal for yielding to that monarch on the question of the Investiture.

But I am now a very old man, and I have only one desire: to be with Christ, and also with our Holy Father Paschal, whom I can never forget.

I will now proceed with what I have to write down, and this again concerns the secret history of the young Cardinal Pier Leone.

When our Sovereign Pontiff from France sent for me, I thought it was because he wished to consult me about the resolution he intends to proclaim at the forthcoming Synod. The resolution reads thus: "The Pope may be judged by no man, nor may anyone cause him distress." (I confess that this resolution has come as a great surprise to me, precisely because it is being proposed by the former Archbishop Guy of Vienne). However, it was not about this resolution that our Sovereign Pontiff wished to consult me, but about the secret conversation which, as he had been informed, the Holy Father Paschal had had with me, before the elevation of the young Pier Leone to the purple.

I informed him that the Holy Father had imposed absolute silence on me in regard to the matter of that conversation.

Whereupon our Sovereign Pontiff from France (in the imperious manner into which he so easily slipped): "He who imposed silence on you then; now commands you to speak."

I understood what he meant, and accordingly told him everything. I did not like doing so, however, for I am only a man after all, and it always pains me to see our Sovereign Pontiff from France in the place of the Holy Father Paschal. And our Sovereign Pontiff for his part understood my feelings in the matter.

During our conversation we passed into the great *aula* of the Lateran Palace, where painters have recently been engaged to represent upon the walls all the Popes who took part in the great Investiture struggle now brought to such a triumphant close; each of them recognizable in the features that were his when he lived and moved among us, arrayed in the pontifical robes, with the tiara on his head, the Holy Father Paschal having in addition a green crown hanging above him in the gold heaven of the picture, on which were inscribed the words of the Concordat of Worms. (This crown also astonished me greatly, for despite my great love for the Holy Father Paschal, I do not regard him, but our new Sovereign Pontiff from France, as the man who brought this great struggle to its triumphant conclusion.)

Our Sovereign Pontiff looked at me closely with his intelligent, animated face: "What say you, Brother, to the crown I have had painted above Pope Paschal?"

Myself, with frank sincerity: "I say, Holy Father, that he who is called to the See of St. Peter, receives in all things a new illumination and counsel from the Holy Spirit."

Our Sovereign Pontiff: "You have answered well, Brother." He then informed me that the Emperor Henry felt his end approaching.

Myself: Was this then the secret of the Concordat? (I had always thought, however, that the secret was to be found in the might of our new Sovereign Pontiff and the passing of the Crown of Constantine to the land of France.)

Our Sovereign Pontiff then handed me a letter from the Emperor Henry, and bade me read it.

THE letter of the Emperor Henry:

"...Nevertheless this conflict has not been concerned solely with the Investiture of the Bishops, but it has involved the question of predominance between this world and the other, and consequently the struggle is going on in all parts of the world, but at its deepest in the soul of each individual (for we all withstand Christ). Accordingly we were in no wise persuaded to make peace because of the scepter which the Legate of Ostia transmitted to us, or rather, in so far as we as King were persuaded thereby, it was simply and solely because we had already been persuaded as a soul, through the blessing which Christ had previously bestowed upon us in the hour when we did Him violence in the castle of Trebico. This blessing given *under* violence has been, we firmly believe, *superior* to all violence, whether of King, or Emperor or anyone whomsoever, and therefore we wish to bear witness to this blessing before our end."

Having read the letter I praised Our Lord Jesus Christ with loud voice for having thus accepted, crowned and proclaimed the secret sacrifice of our Holy Father Paschal. Our Sovereign Pontiff let me go on talking until I relapsed into silence of my own accord. He then returned again to the subject of Cardinal Pier Leone, speaking in high terms of his ability, his sagacity, and his zeal for the welfare of Holy Church.

Our Sovereign Pontiff: Was I aware that many people were speaking of him as the future Pope, but that others were accusing him of aiming at the Papal crown?

Myself: I was well aware of this, but I lived in the happy assurance that it would be a long time yet before we need worry about the future Pope.

Our Sovereign Pontiff, pointing to the letter, with a smile which his strangely agitated features sadly belied: "The Emperor Henry is younger than we!"

It then dawned upon me that this conversation really concerned the next Papal election, and that our Sovereign Pontiff had chosen me to be the recipient of his counsels, it being customary for Popes to consult with their brothers when they feel they are soon to be called away.

Greatly upset at his words, I replied: "If this is how you feel, Holy Father, you ought to consult a doctor."

He (stopping me with a wave of his hand): "We have already done so, and that is why we are talking to you now." Then continuing: "We attach no importance whatever to the calumny that is being circulated about Cardinal Pier Leone, but we attach great importance to the way he receives this calumny. If we understand you rightly, Brother, your opinion is this: The purple of this Cardinal has been a question, as the blessing granted to King Henry was a question—the question, that is to say, of Christ. One of these two has answered the question—the other not yet."

Myself: "Yes, one of them has answered it."

Our Sovereign Pontiff: "Well, our opinion is this: that the questions of Pope Paschal do not remain unanswered. There is in fact a third person to whom Pope Paschal put a question, namely, the Archbishop Guy of Vienne, who formerly raised himself up against him, and who now at this hour answers him. And his answer is this: He whose love for Christ is not yet perfect, is loved so much the more perfectly by Christ. Know, Brother, that we do not exclude Cardinal Pier Leone, any more than we have excluded ourself."

And having said this, he dismissed me.

Since that day I no longer say: "Our Sovereign Pontiff from France," but I say: may I be forgiven for not having said in the beginning: Our Holy Father Callixtus."

THE chronicle relates:

In the days when it became known in Rome that the Holy Father Callixtus was suffering from a mortal disease, the two Frangipani began clearing away the debris of their castle by Sancta Maria Nova, and when the news spread that he was dying, the Frangipani of Septemsolia came over with their people to help them, and when he was carried to the grave, those of Gradellis and of the isle of Lycaonia also appeared with their men and joined in the work. And so there was suddenly seen in the Forum a swarming and crawling of hands and feet, as though the castle were going to rise up out of its ruins with a single bound, so to speak. Day and night we heard the axes at work up on the Palatine, where they were hewing stone blocks from the walls of the palaces of the Caesars, so that it was as if a continuous avalanche were descending upon the valley. Once again, too, our grammarians were to be seen rushing about wringing their hands and imploring mercy for the old columns which were being ruthlessly hewn down like dead trees in a forest. The workmen derived a great deal of fun out of them, and not a few considerable profit; for, as always happens in Rome when large building operations are in progress, the grammarians promptly clubbed together to ransom from the axe the columns on whose preservation they set most store. It seems to us, however, that the workmen always know already which these are, for they invariably make as if to start on them. And that in turn causes us a great deal of amusement.

Meanwhile, however, the people had gathered together, and were likewise wringing their hands and raising their voices in supplication: "Nowhere else in the whole world," they cried, "do the people freely expose themselves to the same evil twice. Why should we Romans always have to plunge into the same tearing torrent?"

They then paraded through the streets, shouting and threatening: Rome must follow the example of the Lombard cities! The people must subdue the captains, otherwise there would never be peace!

When they heard these demonstrations, the Tusculans said: "Everywhere now the masses are beginning to feel their power; on no account, however, can we allow them to exercise it. For, as it seems to us, even in the great epoch of our Pagan ancestors, which must always remain the model for Rome, it was the heads that ruled and not the feet or the hands. Nevertheless if we are to keep the latter quiet we must see to it that the nobles do not create another scandal like that at Sancta Maria in Palara. Let us then suggest to the cardinals that they hold their conclave in the quarter of the Pier Leoni; in this way we shall best show the Frangipani that we do not intend to tolerate another of their escapades."

Accordingly they took this suggestion to Cardinal Heimericus, who was the Chancellor of Pope Callixtus.

FROM the archives of our golden city of Rome:

At that time people could be heard on all sides saying: Take care, or the Frangipani will once again make the fortunes of the Pier Leoni. In truth, we all felt that there was nothing else for the cardinals to do but to seek speedy refuge behind the high walls of the Pier Leone castle so as to protect their conclave from the opposition of the Frangipani. Speaking for ourselves, however, we jumped at the idea, and our eager desires clung to it as to a Jacob's ladder; every night we dreamed we saw the Cardinal Pier Leone crowned with the tiara pass through the wretched ruins of our streets, which at his passing sparkled with the gold he scattered with full hands, so that our heart within us laughed for joy. It was now that the words "the golden Pope" sprang into circulation among us, and it was just as if a heavy bright new bezant started rolling along all the streets of our city.

Meanwhile the Cardinal-Chancellor asked the two Tusculans and Stephanus Normannus if they knew where the Frangipani had procured the money to rebuild their castle. The Tusculans: They had been informed that Petrus Leonis had come to the help of Jacoba Frangipane by the purchase of some rings, for which moreover he had paid a sum of money that would have easily sufficed to buy up all the jewelry in Rome. They did not know whether Petrus Leonis had done this out of Christian charity or because he wanted to buy his peace with the Frangipani.

The Chancellor Heimericus remained silent.

When they were outside, Stephanus Normannus said to the Tusculans: "There is a third interpretation that may be given to the conduct of

Petrus Leonis in this business, but as we are now on his side, it is not for us to unmask him."

One of the Tusculans in reply: "There is no need for us to do so anyway. If, as Jacoba Frangipane now pretends, Petrus Leonis really paid for the armed preparations of her cousins, in order to force the cardinals to take refuge under his wing, the Chancellor Heimericus will be the first to see through his scheme, for that worthy is not only smarter than we are, but unless I am much mistaken, he is even smarter than Petrus Leonis."

THE Cardinal-Chancellor Heimericus, titular of Sancta Maria Nova.

In appearance he resembled one of those statues which, as we know, are erected over the doors of cathedrals in the land of France and on the Rhine: figure stiff and erect; a face as if cut in fine white stone, taciturn but bold, and, according to his enemies, crafty; beneath his brow, as if nestling there, two northern-grey falcons, like the eyes of Pope Callixtus, with whom he had come from France.

It has been said that one day his master sent him a peremptory command to leave his cloister and accompany him to Rome, that his own inclination still called him even today to the peaceful seclusion of Citeaux or Clairvaux, and that he sacrifices himself only out of obedience to the Curia. But we in Rome shook our heads at such reports, because of all our cardinals there was not one, even among those from foreign parts, who wore his purple in such princely fashion as the Cardinal-Chancellor Heimericus.

THE Cardinal-Chancellor Heimericus, titular of Sancta Maria Nova.

For a long time, however, the character of this cardinal remained an enigma to us. At first we said of him: "Great lords" (by which we meant Pope Callixtus) "usually like to have about them none but willing hands ready at all times to execute their commands. Our Sovereign Pontiff has made a point of having a Chancellor who looks the part, but it is obvious that he does not seek his counsel, since we have hardly ever heard the

Chancellor speak with our own ears; moreover on the rare occasions when he has opened his lips he has been sparing of words and unimpressive, his plain discourse being delivered in a toneless voice and leaving his mouth with difficulty."

On the death of Pope Callixtus, however, the Chancellor promptly took everything into his own hands, in such a way that no one was able to oppose him. And precisely the same thing happened on the death of Pope Honorius and during the latter's long illness. But in the interval, as long as Pope Honorius ruled, the Cardinal-Chancellor remained silent, as in the days of Pope Callixtus. During all that time we were only aware of him with our eyes.

THE Cardinal-Chancellor Heimericus, titular of Sancta Maria Nova.

But we had no great love for this cardinal, for we sometimes thought that he secretly despised us, so imperious was his bearing at all times. This, however, he could not alter, as God had made him so.

The story is told that one of his brother cardinals once asked him in annoyance, whether his conscience never convicted him of *superbia*, as he strode along in such high and mighty style.

The Chancellor replied: God had given him to suffer with patience and humility, that throughout his life everyone should think he beheld this sin incarnate in him.

THE Cardinal-Chancellor Heimericus and the Cardinal Pier Leone.

Cardinal Pier Leone had a special affection for Cardinal Heimericus. He said of him that he was the personification of justice and reasonableness in all his dealings and towards all men, and nothing pleased him more than to have their names coupled together. At first, however, the Chancellor felt no such affection for Cardinal Pier Leone, and he only became his friend and protector after the election of Pope Honorius. Accordingly with regard to that election we say: the one great defeat of the Pier Leoni was their final, decisive victory.

THE Cardinal-Chancellor Heimericus to his colleagues.

He spoke as follows:

"Here in Rome as all over the world, a great deal of money is spent on worthless, nay harmful, things. Are we to regard it as reprehensible if once in a way someone uses his money to procure for himself and his family such a noble thing as peace? Or are we to blame a man for helping the enemies he has overcome to rise to their feet again? It does not beseem us to think evil of anyone without proof, but in order that we may act with proper prudence in regard to the reputation of our brother Pier Leone, let us hold our conclave in a place which is not in the district where his family resides."

At those words, some of the cardinals remembered, like the Tusculans, the election at Sancta Maria in Palara, and said, as the people before them had done: "No one submits of his own free will to the same mischief twice."

The Chancellor: Holy Church did not fear mischief; what she feared was that the will of Christ might be crossed. He knew also that the Frangipani had heard how everyone was saying that the reconstructions they were engaged in were being paid for by Petrus Leonis; in his opinion, therefore, their hands would henceforth be tied.

Then the cardinals said to each other: "Our brother Heimericus mistrusts our brother Pier Leone more than he does the Frangipani, although our late Sovereign Pontiff and Father did not wish us to exclude him from our confidence."

Whereupon the Chancellor: Neither did he wish to exclude him; he excluded nobody, but God had not endowed him with the gift of reading souls; all he possessed was a calm and shrewd mind, and it was his duty therefore to be guided by that. If he was wrong, might God vouchsafe to enlighten him; in which case he would not hesitate to admit his error.

After further consultation they decided to withdraw to the Church of Saint Pancratius, which lies on the other side of the Tiber.

THE chronicle relates:

As they drew near the said church, they found the ground already occupied by the whole fighting strength of the Pier Leoni which had been hastily summoned and assembled there by the Tusculans (so great was the apprehension of these last); at their head Petrus Leonis himself together with his six sons. With regard to the latter our captains were wont to say: They stand in womanish clothes on the turrets of their towers and gaze down with cynical amusement on our battles, boasting that they will never fight save in defence of Holy Church. And so today they were all there, sitting their magnificent chargers very badly, and like their father looking extremely uncomfortable in their unaccustomed coats of mail.

Petrus Leonis, lowering his sword in presence of the cardinals: He was proud and happy to protect their venerable assembly; they could dispose of him and his riders as they pleased and thought fit.

Then all the riders likewise lowered their swords, so that it was as if a field of iron corn ears were bending before a gust of wind, and the coats of mail gleamed and rustled round the walls of Saint Pancratius like a stream of grey water. The heart of more than one member of the assembly misgave him at the sight of such powerful protection.

The Cardinal Pier Leone, however, soon put these misgivings to rest with his smooth, suave tongue: His brother cardinals and he thanked his father for this great and ready proof of his goodwill, but they did not need his assistance, and if he asked them where they wished these riders to go, their answer was that the best thing would be for them to return to their homes and not worry about the conclave.

Whereupon Petrus Leonis turned quietly to his followers and bade them obey the Cardinal's command and ride home.

The cardinals among themselves: "See, how unjust everyone always is to the Pier Leoni! And we are no better than the rest, even though we try not to be unjust to anybody. They seem, however, to know how to bear their wrongs in a Christian spirit. But this was the sign to which our dying Sovereign Pontiff made allusion, if we have understood our brother Petrus of Portus rightly."

THE chronicle relates:

Meanwhile the serpent of Jacoba Frangipane sprang back into the lap of its mistress; in other words the rumor that the Frangipani had been bought by the Pier Leoni had become known in the castle by Sancta Maria Nova. Cencius and Leo were beside themselves with rage and sorrow, and yelled at the top of their voices: "This is the work of Petrus Leonis! It is his doing! The trick of a cunning Jew!"

Jacoba: "No, no, it is the act of someone who means you well. Can you not see that this rumor will cause the assembly of cardinals to break away from Petrus Leonis?"

They: "But it protects them in the distant place they have retired to, for if we pursue them people will promptly say of us: You see, they force them back to Petrus Leonis, which proves that he has bought them and paid them cash down! And this our honor could never tolerate! It means then that we are reduced to the role of helpless spectators, and cannot move even if a Pier Leone is elected Pope at St. Pancratius!"

Jacoba: "It means nothing of the kind, but it means that you must raise your protests otherwise than at Sancta Maria in Palara. Copy the example of Petrus Leonis, who owes much of his success to the fact that he is forever sounding the trumpet of piety."

Cencius and Leo: "Jacoba, we cannot lie!"

She: "In that case, you must betray Rome!"

At this they both burst into tears.

FROM the Notes of the Cardinal-Bishop Petrus of Portus.

...But this also forms part of the Cross of Jesus Christ! For well we know that the lot of the Bridegroom upon earth must be repeated for all time and in all things in His Bride, our Holy Church, in order that the successive generations may learn, believe and understand: given into the hands of men, and entangled by them in the play of their earthly ends— for they have also sought to make Christ a King of this world—verily she has been delivered up to the Passion of her Master and Bridegroom: rejected with Him in His rejection, derided with Him in His derision, suffering with Him the violence that He suffered, in order that she may one day be victorious with Him in His victory!

And that is why I also record the election of our Holy Father Honorius II (but if I speak of it, it is because of the question put by Pope Paschal to our brother Pier Leone).

The people are furious at not having received their "Golden Pope," and they are saying: the Frangipani are villains. In my view, however, they are still just big, turbulent children, even though they are becoming more prudent as they grow older. Thus, they no longer shouted as at Sancta Maria in Palara: "Let us seize the false and foreign Bishop of Rome!" But with resounding voices they raised the cry: "We do not want a Pope of Jewish blood! The wise and holy Bishop Lambert of Ostia, he is worthy to be the Father of Christendom."

Now with regard to our brother Lambert, we all say of him: In truth he is a great and pious priest of Jesus Christ, a steadfast and able servant of His Holy Church, which owes him thanks for the concordat with the Emperor Henry! None of us therefore could contradict the Frangipani; at the same time none of us could support them, for the decree of Pope Nicholas prohibits lay folk from recording their votes at the election of our Holy Father the Pope, be these votes ever so wisely directed. Accordingly our brother Heimericus invited the Frangipani to keep silence and to leave us at once.

But they only shouted the louder: If the wise and holy Bishop Lambert were not elected, it would show that we were all enemies of Holy Church; they however (drawing their swords) would fight for her.

At these words the hearts of some of our brothers failed them, and taking the purple mantle worn by the Pope, they hastily threw it over the shoulders of our brother Lambert (he collapsed under its weight as under the red wound of a sword), to save us all from being seized and dragged away by the intruders as at Sancta Maria in Palara.

These then burst into shouts of jubilation, and hastened to announce to the city the name of the Pope whom they now assumed to have been elected.

As soon as we were alone, our brother Lambert—he still lay on his knees, as if borne to the ground by the weight of the mantle—begged us with tears in his voice to remove from his shoulders the intolerable burden of the pontifical robe forcibly thrust upon him, and so undo the part we had played in this monstrous impiety. But we found it hard to grant his request, for it went against our hearts to divest our grey-haired and venerable brother of the mantle, when we ourselves had placed it upon him. So we all turned with a look of inquiry to our brother Heimericus.

Meanwhile, however, as if unable to bear its burden a moment longer, our brother Lambert struggled free of the mantle, himself seizing hold of it as if he were tearing from his shoulders a flaming brand and crushing it out with his hands; and now the mantle lay about his knees like a bouquet of glowing red embers, and we were all of us so moved that hot tears came into our eyes.

Suddenly we again heard the smooth, suave voice of our brother Pier Leone. Hitherto he had remained seated at the back, but he now pushed his way to the front, and picking up the mantle, addressed us:

"Reverend and dear Brothers! It seems to me that the dignity of our brother Lambert of Ostia stands so high, that neither before God nor man can it suffer or lose in the slightest degree, even though rude and lawless laymen use it as a battle cry. I therefore give my vote for our wise and venerable brother Lambert of Ostia."

We all of us then expressed our hearty agreement with our brother Pier Leone. And thus our brother Lambert was clothed with the pontifical purple for the second time.

After which we intoned the *Te Deum*....

Later, our brother Heimericus turned to me: He had previously said that he would not be afraid to admit it, if he made a mistake. Well, he had made a mistake about the Frangipani. But what did I now think in regard to the Pier Leoni?

Myself (surprised that he should still ask me): I thought that our brother Pier Leone had acted with zeal and dignity in the presence of us all.

He: Yes, he had acted with zeal.

Myself: Of course everyone had his own way of doing things. But here, the deed and the word both did our brother great credit.

He: Most certainly; the mind, however, was capable of interesting itself in all things, that was its essential character.

Myself: As regards the essential character of the mind, he (our brother Heimericus) knew more about that than I did.

He (with a strange expression of humility on his proud face): That was precisely why he was now consulting me.

Myself: If he were asking for the opinion of my heart, its answer would be this: "Granted that the mind can in actual fact interest itself in all things, nevertheless it can never be the effective cause of our being moved in our deepest selves."

He: Had our brother Pier Leone moved me today?

Myself: Yes, he had moved me, and it was by the suffering that showed on his face, when the Frangipani cried out that they did not want a Pope of Jewish blood.

He: He had felt the same thing. Then, in a low voice: "St. Peter too was a son of Israel."

From that hour our brother Heimericus gave his friendship to our brother Pier Leone without reserve, and so pointedly did he show his esteem for him and expatiate on his brilliant gifts, that people soon began saying that he intended one day to propose him for Pope.

IX

FROM an old letter which Rabbi Nathan Ben Jechiel wrote: "But we are like ships sunk in the seas, and over our heads pass the ships of others."

THE women of the Jews:

In Rome they do not count the years, for so many things have happened there; we are all of us, old and young, only chaff before the winds of time, and those who carry seventy years on their head, are in the face of this city like new-born children. And Israel likewise does not count the years. (For where should we begin to count? Shall we begin with the stars over the head of our father Abraham or with the grains of sand on the desert of Bersaba?) Yet sometimes it has seemed to us that a very long time has passed since the day when Ibn Mischal made his prophecy by the bedside of Miriam. When we said to Nathan ben Jechiel: "Rabbi, you are very old," he replied: "Yes, I am very old, for it is written: The days of our years are three score and ten years, and if they reach to fourscore years, that is a great age." And when we said to Hannah Naemi: "Hannah Naemi, you are very old," she replied: "Yes, I am very old, and the Lord will soon take me to Him." But when we said to Miriam: "Miriam, you too have now grown old," she replied: "I have been old for a long time now." For Miriam did not wish to be reminded that the prophecy still remained unfulfilled. But when we said to Trophäea: "You have grown older," she replied: "Indeed, I am not yet old enough."

For Trophäea also had not yet become reconciled to her destiny. But we remained silent, when Miriam and Trophäea spoke thus, for we believed in the hope of neither the one nor the other. We among ourselves: "These two are lost like Israel in her expectation. Daily, men sink into the grave and women die, and still the Messiah comes not. And so likewise the strength of this woman is failing, and this maiden's bloom is withering away."

THE women of the Jews relate:
When foreign Jews came to Rome and asked to see Miriam's bridal jewels, it often happened that these could not be shown them, as Trophäea had secretly taken them away and hidden them in her room. Miriam thought that when she was alone she decked herself out with them, thus gratifying, at least in play, her defiant wish to enjoy the sensation of wearing the gold rings on her fingers and the chains round her neck and the crown on her head. But looking through the key-hole one day, she saw that Trophäea was merely feeling the treasures tenderly and timidly with her hands, and bedewing the old gold with her tears.

HANNAH Naemi to Miriam: "Leave her alone, Miriam, she has only her sorrow to comfort her and the hardness of her lot to soften her."
However, Trophäea's mouth was as if every day handed it a goblet of myrrh.

THE women of the Jews relate:
Hannah Naemi to Trophäea (while the latter was playing with the old trinkets): "Trophäea, I am old and nearing the grave, but do you think I could have grown so old, if I had not still been able to love my dead husband? For it is not indispensable to a woman that she should be loved, but it is indispensable to her that she should love. If only you could love someone you would be saved."
Trophäea: "Aunt, I can now no longer love anyone."

THE women of the Jews relate:

Hannah Naemi to Rabbi Nathan ben Jechiel:

"Tell me, Brother, in order that I may not sin against the Lord in my old days! The heart of this maiden was like an open casket of trustfulness and like a precious vase of tenderness. Now the casket is empty, and the vase is broken—we have all become blind with her in a blind world! Explain it to me, Brother, that I may not sin against the Lord, for it seems to me that He mocks us!"

THE Jews of Rome relate:

In those days Rabbi Elchanan came to Rome for the last time, accompanied by his two favorite disciples. These no longer let him travel alone, for although Rabbi Elchanan's nose still hung over his face like a bold blade, the face itself was all over wrinkles, furrowed and ravaged like a battlefield, when evening descends. His disciples said: "Our master is old, and we do not want him to die without revealing his last truth to us. For we know that he keeps locked in his breast a truth that is more precious than all the truths he has hitherto revealed to us. But when we ask him: 'Master, why do you hide your treasure from our eyes? Are we not yet worthy to behold it?' he replies: 'Have still a little patience! For every truth consists of two parts: one is recognition, the other assent. But I have not yet assented.' And so we follow him whithersoever he wanders, so as to be ready at any hour to receive his truth when he calls us."

But there was at that time yet a third person who followed the steps of Rabbi Elchanan; it was he whom we afterwards called the "Hater."

THE Jews of Rome relate:

We do not know who spread the report that it was on account of Trophäea that Rabbi Elchanan came to Rome at this time, but the story went that he came because he felt a desire to converse once again before his end with her who as a little child years ago had said to him: The crown of David has wings. While he and his disciples were seated at table with Rabbi Nathan ben Jechiel—it was already evening, and the candles shed their soft light over the room—he asked Miriam about her daughter and whether they had followed his advice and allowed her to be instructed. (Trophäea was not with them at table, but was sitting alone in her room, for there were days when her melancholy overcame her, and this was one of them.)

Miriam: "Yes, to be sure, Rabbi Elchanan, we followed your advice; we had my daughter instructed in the sacred doctrine of the masters with the young men in the school. We failed her in nothing, left nothing undone that might prepare her to be the instrument of the Lord. And the Lord—praise be to Him—also prepared her, for in making her blind he put the mark of His will upon her. But she herself rose against the Lord—praise be to Him—and thus everything we did for her has remained vain to this hour. For the Lord—praise be to Him—gives the promise, certainly, but its fulfillment rests with man."

Rabbi Elchanan: "Yes, Miriam, the Lord—praise be to Him—gives the promise; and it is for man to fulfill it, but the name of this fulfillment the Lord again reserves unto Himself—praise be to Him in all eternity."

While Rabbi Elchanan was speaking, the door opened, and darkest night entered.

THE Jews of Rome relate:

As we have previously related, Rabbi Elchanan was not the only Jew who was saved from the city of Jerusalem when it fell into the hands of the Crusading army, but there was one other whom we beheld later, and of whom it is said that he escaped into vengeance as Rabbi Elchanan into love.

No sooner had the stranger entered—he came in noiselessly and stealthily, like thieves and assassins when they steal into a house by night—than Elchanan's two disciples started up out of their seats in terror, for they well knew that this man was pursuing their master; but Rabbi Nathan and his family started up in surprise, for they thought that a second Rabbi Elchanan was standing before them.

RABBI Elchanan and the Stranger.

Rabbi Elchanan's nose was, as we have said, like a noble blade of Damascus, but the Stranger's nose was like the sharp beak of a vulture. Rabbi Elchanan's face recalled the ravages of a battlefield, the face of the Stranger the desolation of a place of execution. Rabbi Elchanan's eyes were like two expiring torches, but the Stranger's eyes were like flaming pitch. And thus they were like two vessels, molded by the same potter and formed of the same clay, one for honor, the other for dishonor, so that whoever beheld them together could not but be startled at both their likeness and their unlikeness to each other.

THE Jews of Rome relate:

Meanwhile the Stranger addressed Rabbi Elchanan: "At last I have found you, Apostate! Long enough have I been following you from place to place, and now that I have tracked you down, you shall never again escape me!" Then turning to Rabbi Nathan ben Jechiel: "Woe to you, Rabbi Nathan, for little do you know whom you are sheltering under your roof, but I will tell you. Know then, that this man was with me in the city of Jerusalem, when the savage Crusaders shut up six hundred of our brothers and sisters in their burning Synagogue. *Him*, however, one of those murderous Goyim hid in his house and saved (I wager he will have wrung from him a pretty sum of money for doing so); and since then he has gone about saying that his rescuer prayed with him to the same God whom Israel prays to, aye, and that the promise given to our father Abraham has been fulfilled in the children of Edom, but that Israel must be ready to pour out its blood, if only the Name of the Lord may be praised among the nations. Come then, cast him out of the Synagogue, Rabbi Nathan, and pronounce judgment upon him, for he blasphemes the Law and the Name of the Lord!"

Rabbi Nathan ben Jechiel under his white hairs: "Let Rabbi Elchanan speak!"

Rabbi Elchanan, in his evening countenance the whole battle of the departed day surging up once again: "Rabbi Nathan ben Jechiel, I have not yet assented."

Rabbi Nathan ben Jechiel: "Go then and sleep in peace under my roof, Rabbi Elchanan!"

THE Jews of Rome relate:

Now when Rabbi Elchanan had retired (as regards his disciples, they had departed with the Stranger, for they wanted to defend their master against him), Rabbi Nathan ben Jechiel spoke as follows: "Hannah Naemi and Miriam, I desire you this evening to leave the door of the house unlocked, and if during the night you think you hear someone furtively go out or come in you are not to get up to see who it is, but you are to remain in your rooms, for the Lord Himself will watch over the house this night." (Rabbi Nathan ben Jechiel gave these orders because he thought that Rabbi Elchanan intended to slip away secretly during the night.) Accordingly Hannah Naemi and Miriam left the door of the house unlocked, and when they heard the steps of Rabbi Elchanan, they did not get up, but remained obediently in their beds. Rabbi Elchanan had in fact quite understood what Rabbi Nathan meant to propose to him when he invited him to sleep this one night under his roof. However, just as he was making his way out of the house with all the haste his weary old limbs were capable of, the "Hater" fell upon him and struck him down in the darkness. And so it was the Lord's will that Rabbi Elchanan should carry out his intention of beholding the face of Trophäea once again.

Now Trophäea knew nothing about the Rabbi Nathan's orders, consequently when she heard groaning in the vestibule she got up, thinking that perhaps Hannah Naemi had fallen down in one of her attacks of giddiness. She groped her way to where the groans came from and knelt down beside the prostrate form on the floor.

Trophäea (passing her hand over the body beside her): "Oh, Rabbi Elchanan, it is you! Speak, what has happened to you?"

Just at that moment the moon came out from behind the clouds and shone through the window of the vestibule on Trophäea's face.

Rabbi Elchanan: "Oh, you beautiful, blind face! Blind face that saw the crown of David!"

Trophäea, strangely moved by his tone: "Alas, Rabbi Elchanan, I no longer see crown or wings! Around me is nothing but night!"

Rabbi Elchanan, thrice: "Yes, yes, yes!"

Trophäea: "Rabbi Elchanan, what do you mean? To whom are you saying 'yes' with such fervor?"

Rabbi Elchanan (dying): "To you, Trophäea!"

At that moment Rabbi Nathan ben Jechiel called out from his room: "Oh, Rabbi Elchanan, I hear you say 'yes,' have you then assented?"

But no reply came from the lips of Rabbi Elchanan.

Then Trophäea understood that Rabbi Elchanan was dying, and she raised his head from the hard floor on to her lap. And so Rabbi Elchanan passed away....

All this happened shortly before Trophäea went to the palace of Petrus Leonis.

X

———————◆———————

From the Archives of our Golden City of Rome: Petrus Leonis was now grown old and fat. His battles lay behind him and the day of his wishes was fulfilled; these last as punctually and surely realized as the big payments and repayments which stood registered in the heavy parchment rolls of his counting-house over a period of thirty years and more. Never yet had it happened to Petrus Leonis to have to register a loss, for he had never made a mistake in his calculations; on the other hand he had often had the good sense and fairness not to press for payment, but to grant a long delay in the settlement of his claims.

When Pope Callixtus died, it was said among the people that Petrus Leonis had granted a delay in the settlement of his claims, but when Pope Honorius lay dying, some of us said: this time he will attain his end, for he has the Cardinal-Chancellor Heimericus behind him. Indeed the latter was at that time the most powerful man in the Curia, for Pope Honorius had been on a sick-bed for a whole year, and everyone fixed his eyes solely on his Chancellor, in whose hands lay the care and administration of all the affairs of Holy Church.

And thus the whole city of Rome was awaiting with joy the advent of the "Golden Pope." But in the palace of the Pier Leoni everyone was rejoicing except the old Rachel, for she, like Miriam, thought day and night about the son of Petrus Leonis, for whose sake she had once bitten the flag-stones of the church, when they were baptizing her.

THE old Rachel.

It was often said later that they ought to have turned Rachel out of the palace years before, at the time, that is to say, when the rumor was going about that the boy entrusted to her had been secretly circumcised by her agency. But Petrus Leonis had not turned Rachel out at that time, some say out of Christian charity, but others say: Jewish blood never lets Jewish blood perish, no matter how great the cost to itself. It cost Petrus Leonis a great deal, however, to keep the old Rachel.

THE old Rachel.

Among the servants of the palace the story went round that Petrus Leonis never liked meeting the old Rachel, but that Rachel on the contrary was always trying to meet Petrus Leonis, and that the more he showed he did not wish to have anything to do with her, the more she forced herself on his notice.

Rachel was now very old; she had no teeth left with which to bite the ground as at her baptism. This gave her a good excuse for saying she could not eat pigs' flesh. Also she was so decrepit that they made allowances if she did not appear at Holy Mass in the morning, or if her hands rested from work on a weekday as well (namely the Sabbath). Nevertheless, the people of the palace all said of her that she was secretly a Jewess, and the other maids refused to share their quarters with her. Accordingly, Donna Bona had given her a tiny room at the end of the long corridor through which one approaches the eastern tower. Whenever Petrus Leonis wanted to go up there, Rachel issued unexpectedly from her door and got in his way.

The servants who accompanied Petrus Leonis to the tower: "Take yourself off, old owl, the illustrious Consul cannot bear the sight of you."

Rachel, however, did not take herself off, but fluttering like an old sick bat, mounted the steps in front of Petrus Leonis. Then Petrus Leonis looked away, pretending not to see her.

"Our Master is very kind to the old fool," said the servants among themselves; but one of them who had observed Petrus Leonis closely, said: "No, our master is ashamed."

Whereupon one of the others: "Why should our master be ashamed? He has attained everything that is to be attained upon earth, and if his son is going to be Pope, as everyone says, he will have heaven opened to him as well."

It was because of this word, as we believe, that Rachel went to see Miriam, at the time, namely, when Petrus Leonis lay dying. For as sometimes happens when a man thinks he stands at the end of all his desires, so also here: God then decrees the man's own end.

And so it was that Petrus Leonis died before Pope Honorius.

THE remarkable and terrifying death of the great Petrus Leonis.

Petrus Leonis died some days before Pope Honorius, but not like the latter after a long and wearisome illness; but he fell down with a sudden seizure on the battlements of the Moles Hadriani, where he was making his dispositions regarding the militia and standard-bearers who were destined to protect the forthcoming election of the Sovereign Pontiff; for the personal physician of the Holy Father had told him that very day that the decease of the august invalid was imminent.

THE chronicle relates:

When Petrus Leonis collapsed, there was no one beside him save a foreign crusader who had returned from the Holy Land to report to Christendom upon the affairs of the kingdom of Jerusalem. He had already sought speech with Petrus Leonis on the previous day, but had been refused admittance. Some say that Petrus Leonis had a presentiment that this man was destined to be present at the hour of his death; but this is not true, for Petrus Leonis was always clear-headed and never experienced those strange, haunting fears and forebodings which some of us now and again suffer from. The most that can be said is that he always disliked the presence of crusaders, although he had done so much for the transport of the holy army to the East. According to others, however, this particular crusader was not really a crusader at all, but a Jew in disguise, and the very same man who had been dogging the steps of Rabbi Elchanan. Be that as it may, the knight was never afterwards seen in Rome, but he vanished as suddenly as he came, and moreover, without seeking out the cardinals and other princes of Rome, as he had previously declared his intention of doing.

THE Crusading Knight (according to the story about him that passes among the people).

When Petrus Leonis arrived with his suite at the Moles Hadriani, the strange knight was standing in the shadow of this ancient sepulcher, and just as the former was about to pass through the gate, he stepped out into the open and abruptly confronted him. The men with Petrus Leonis were at once struck by the remarkable resemblance he bore to their master; the two might have been brothers, or it was as if a mirror had suddenly been held before Petrus Leonis in which he beheld his own features. For a moment Petrus Leonis was himself too startled to proceed; he then tried to hurry past the unknown knight. The latter, however, asked to be allowed to accompany him, saying that the matter he had to settle with him would not take long. Whereupon Petrus Leonis, who was always courteous and obliging, invited him to ascend the battlements with him. There, for a few moments, he stood alone with him in conversation. What passed between them we do not know. The watchman who heard the two of them talking in the distance caught only the word "Justice," uttered by the strange knight. A moment later, so he affirms, Petrus Leonis fell to the ground.

THE chronicle relates:

They bore the poor little body, which though never beautiful or imposing, had always held itself with great dignity, from the Moles Hadriani to its own home, for it was remembered that Petrus Leonis had often expressed a wish to die in the bed where he had once had the signal honor of enabling the Holy Father Urban II to close his eyes in peace.

Amid the tears and laments of his children and of all his servants and retainers (for Petrus Leonis had been loved and respected in his house by everyone down to the lowest menial) they carried the dying man into the sumptuous bed-chamber of his palace, planted the golden senatorial mitre, which had tumbled off when he fell, all askew on his massive patriarchal head, and laid him solemnly down on the bed of state, on which years before the Holy Father Urban II had passed away.

Meanwhile the news of the event had spread like wildfire through the whole city, and a large number of people had flocked to the Pier Leone palace, so that the bed-chamber and all the stairs leading down into the court were crowded with men and women on their knees praying. Even the Cardinal-Chancellor Heimericus had hurried away from the sick-bed of his master to accord the dying man the honor of his presence and the consolation of his prayers. But among the members of the nobility present were several who had never been seen there before; this was because everyone thought that in a few days Cardinal Pier Leone would be elected Pope, and it was felt therefore that the dying hour of the great Petrus Leonis was no less glorious in its way than that of Pope Urban.

THE dying Petrus Leonis.

Meanwhile the gilded columns of the magnificent couch towered lightly and unconcernedly over the dying man, who lay beneath them heavy as a stone. His face was blue and puffed out, and sweat stood on his brow; his large, swollen mouth hung sideways, and slavered over the purple cushions on which his head rested; he had lost the power of speech.

He was given Extreme Unction. The Cardinal, his son, administered it to him with his own hands, weeping like the rest, for he thought his father was already on the point of expiring. But as he made the Sign of the Cross on his forehead, Petrus Leonis suddenly opened his eyes wide, and surveyed the people around him, like a man who perceives clearly, but with astonishment, that something is happening to him of which he cannot make the slightest sense.

The dying man with a rattle in his throat (but it was as though a captive were making a gigantic effort to burst his bonds): "Bless…I would like to bless…"

They signed to his children, who advanced in pairs, the dying man being raised on his pillows, so that he could place his hand on them as they knelt there. Again the captive was seen struggling with his lips, but no sound issued therefrom save an unintelligible babbling and gurgling. Suddenly, however, his indomitable will obtained the mastery over his body once again; from the horrible gurgling and mouthing, articulate words forced their way through.

The dying Petrus Leonis: "My children, may you be blessed with the blessing of Abraham and Isaac and Jacob! My children, may the God of our fathers be with you! My children, observe the Law! My children, be true to Israel, our people…"

Everyone went white, including the domestics who thronged the doorways praying for their master, for the whole room had heard these words of Petrus Leonis, but not a soul durst move for terror. And thus they remained standing and kneeling, huddled against each other as if drawn together by the horror that possessed them all, and in the deathly silence that prevailed one seemed to hear the beating of their hearts.

THE chronicle relates:

At last the Cardinal Pier Leone (he was the only person there who retained his composure) stood up and spoke: he requested them to leave his father for the present; he proposed with the priests of his suite to begin the Prayers for the Dying, and if they wished, they could all join in from the ante-chamber. (But he was not heard to say a word about his father being no longer in his right mind; on the contrary his manner suggested that what they had just heard, far from being something that needed to be put right, had never happened at all.) While he was still speaking, however, everyone rose hurriedly from his knees, and in a moment he beheld only a scrambling mass of backs and clothes; with so little dignity and decorum did all these people scuttle away in their horror at having heard the great, the devout Petrus Leonis confess Judaism on his death-bed. The Cardinal-Chancellor Heimericus alone stood still, his tall figure calm and erect, and under his brow the two falcons of his eyes transfixing Cardinal Pier Leone, as though they were trying to penetrate his very heart and reins.

At that moment the dying Petrus Leonis made a movement: for the second time the tall golden senatorial mitre fell from his head and rolled like a stiff, empty pasteboard-bag, between the two cardinals on to the middle of the deserted floor.

CARDINAL Pier Leone alone with his dying father.

He kept his eyes fixed on the mitre lying on the floor, as if indeed it was not the mitre of the dying man at all, but that other triple crown which he already felt on his head. The perplexity in his inmost soul, however, had little to do with this fallen mitre, but was something far deeper and more dangerous.

The bed-chamber had two folding-doors leading to the ante-room; they were as large as gates, and each was mounted with bronze lions' heads such as one sees on the gates of the old pagan temples. These the Cardinal now locked to prevent anyone from entering before his father expired. He did this with his own hands, for the two young clerics who had accompanied him had suddenly vanished like the rest. For this he was thankful. He then took up the crucifix which stood on the table by the bed, in order to hold it out to his father, as behooves a priest when he is ministering to a dying man. But while he was holding it in his hands, he was suddenly reminded of a young Patarin who had recently been called before him to vindicate himself concerning the Cross. (For, as is well known, these heretics refuse to pay the crucifix, and, even the particles of the Holy Cross itself, the reverence due to them; the Son of God, they pretend, is not only the Savior on the Cross, but each member of their sect who has received the *Consolamentum*—which is the name they give their heretical sacrament.) The hot iron which the Patarin held in his hand during the ordeal had witnessed against him, and the people had applauded his conviction, but the Cardinal himself had felt strangely drawn to the young heretic.

Cardinal Pier Leone to himself: "Am I then a Patarin like him? Am I then a heretic?"

Meanwhile the dying man had already perceived the cross in the cardinal's hesitating hand. His small, tough body raised itself bolt upright on its bed: "Away—away—what is this?"

The Cardinal (his face was now so white that one would have said he had snow, not blood, under his skin): "Father, are you sending me away to call Donna Bona, your wife?"

But the name Donna Bona seemed to convey nothing to Petrus Leonis. Gasping as if in terrible anguish: "Miriam—where is my wife, Miriam?"

Abruptly from his upright posture, he dropped like an animal on his hands and feet, and crawled, as though jerked along by the convulsions of his death agony, with gruesome haste to the foot of the bed, whence between the two pillars of the open balcony one could see the little Jewish city deep down in the river.

Suddenly it seemed to the Cardinal as if he heard the wailing of a child in the room. He clasped his father in his arms with a gesture of love and anguish (an anguish again which resided in remote and dangerous depths): blood pulsing against blood, face against face, breast against breast, as though a dying torch were bending down towards one that was ablaze, and for the space of a moment were mingled with it in a single flame. At that moment the wailing of the invisible child became a piercing shriek.

Deep down in the Cardinal's soul, these words: "There is the door where the Norman announced the fall of Jerusalem…there is the court where the people cried 'Alleluia'…there is the staircase down which the shrieking boy fled…and here in this room is justice!"

And now the dying torch sprang back and flashed its own light once again.

Petrus Leonis, extending his arms towards the Jewish city, and with a fervor such as one had never heard in the cold and careful calculator: "My people Israel! My people Israel!"

The Cardinal in the depth of his soul (brokenly, but very quickly, as if one flash of lightning after another flared up within him): "I am not a Patarin, I am a Jew! I have never loved Christ, and at this moment I hate Him, for—" The thought broke off abruptly. As from the far distance: "Where then at this hour is the Christ whom you hate?"

Once again, in a voice louder even and more fervent than before, the dying man raised his heartrending cry: "My people Israel! My people Israel!"

Suddenly it seemed to the Cardinal as if a voice at his side said: "*Gesta Dei per Petrum Leonis—*" Coming abruptly to himself: "What does all this mean? Is my father lying in his death agony or am I? What does it mean to hate Christ? My family have served the Church that bears His name with all their strength. Are not the people right when they demand a powerful Pope?"

He again embraced his father, in order to force him back on to his pillows. Now, however, it was no longer as a moment ago, flame meeting flame, and blood meeting blood, but the dying man seemed to discern a strange element. With the terrible strength of life's last breath, he resisted his son. Still louder than before: "My people—my people Israel!"

The Cardinal to himself: "They will hear his cry out in the hall—it is no use the doors being shut, if he does not keep quiet. But how can I make him keep quiet?"

At that moment he perceived the old Rachel.

THE old Rachel.

She entered the large bed-chamber from the back, where there is no door, but the two red curtains between which one passes into the room that had once been Miriam's. Advancing with her old, shuffling steps, Rachel went straight up to her master, just as if, instead of having avoided her all these years, he had actually been awaiting her for years and years.

The dying man: "Rachel, have you come at last? Where is my wife Miriam?"

Rachel: "Master, she fled to her father, Rabbi Nathan ben Jechiel, the day you allowed yourself to be baptized."

But all this was lost on the sick man. With veiled eyes, as if he were gazing at his interlocutress through a net, he repeated: "Rachel, go and call my wife..."

A sudden sensation came over the Cardinal, as if hell were whispering into his ear. Aloud: "Rachel, say something to please him! Speak to him of his wife—pretend you are going to fetch her..."

Then Rachel bent once again over the dying Petrus Leonis, and silence reigned in the room. A moment later Rachel went out. But she did not go, as the Cardinal imagined, to deceive Petrus Leonis, but she went in very truth to call Miriam, or in other words, to ruin the Cardinal's hopes.

THE chronicle relates:

During all this while, those assembled in the ante-chamber continued to pray aloud, as Cardinal Pier Leone had requested them to do, their voices interrupted from time to time by the violent sobbings of Donna Bona, who could not contain herself for shame and fury. The Chancellor Heimericus alone quietly left the hall, in order to return to the bedside of Pope Honorius.

As he was crossing one of the large, dark courts of the palace—these were all swarming with the horses and riders of the assembled nobility—Cencius and Leo Frangipane suddenly stood in his way. (They had just been informed of what had happened at the death-bed of Petrus Leonis).

The Chancellor remained silent, for he felt quite sure that they wanted to offer him their assistance.

They passed through other dark courts, the two Frangipani walking on either side of the Chancellor, waiting for him to address them; the Chancellor, however, striding along, as though determined to keep his mouth closed, even if it meant walking with his two companions to the end of the world. One of the courts—it was the ancient theater of Marcellus—lay like an open crater in the flank of a high mountain. At all the exits stood armed guards, and behind them on the steps of the theater slept others. The coats of mail clanked, as the guards lowered their weapons to salute the Cardinal. The palace was full of armed men, as the Moles Hadrian! could not contain all those whom Petrus Leonis had summoned for the protection of the forthcoming conclave.

At last Leo Frangipane, when he saw that he and his brother were waiting in vain: What was the final impression that the Cardinal-Chancellor received at the death-bed of the pious Christian Petrus Leonis?

The Chancellor in his toneless voice, frankly but with frigid aloofness: "He was of the opinion that the dying man, in the delirium of his last hours, had lapsed into the language and world of ideas of his childhood."

Leo Frangipane: Would the Cardinal-Chancellor like to know what was going on behind the closed doors?

The Chancellor: No, he was not interested.

Leo Frangipane: He and his brother, however, were very anxious to know, and they were thinking of breaking open the doors.

So saying, they quitted the Chancellor.

THE Jews of Rome relate:

When Rachel arrived at the house of Nathan ben Jechiel, Hannah Naemi and Miriam were sitting together alone. The Rabbi had gone to the school, and Trophäea was in her room; but she was not playing with the old bridal jewels, she was thinking of Rabbi Elchanan.

Trophäea to herself: "O Rabbi Elchanan, why did you die without instructing me? I wanted to ask you why you said *yes* with such fervor to my poor life! If only I could talk like you! O Rabbi Elchanan, why did you die so soon?"

THE Jews of Rome relate:

When Hannah Naemi saw the old Rachel standing in the doorway she started violently and gave a little cry of alarm, for she knew Rachel well; but the Jews are not allowed to have intercourse with those of their race who have been baptized.

Rachel: "You need not recoil from me, Hannah Naemi; they did not think it worthwhile to turn me out; besides I have not come to speak to you, but I seek my former mistress Miriam." (Going up to her.)

Rachel to Miriam: "Woman, Petrus Leonis, your husband, is dying, and you are to go to him at once."

Miriam without looking at Rachel: "I do not know a Petrus Leonis who is my husband. I have no husband, I am unmarried save to my own people of Israel."

Rachel: "You may be unmarried, Woman, but you have a son, and it is he, not Petrus Leonis, who sends me."

When Miriam heard this, she sprang up, like a young gazelle.

Miriam to Rachel: "If it is my son who sends you, he does not mean me (flinging open the door of the room where Trophäea was sitting) but *her*."

To Trophäea: "Daughter, arise, the hour has come: you are to go to your brother!"

Hannah Naemi: "Oh Miriam, you cannot mean this seriously. It would be rash and wicked to send your daughter into the house of Edom."

Miriam: "No, it is not rash and wicked to send her whom the Lord calls."

Hannah Naemi: "Oh Miriam, she is still too beautiful!"

Miriam (like one intoxicated): "No, she is not yet beautiful enough: my son shall know that Israel awaits him like a bride!" To Trophäea: "Daughter, unlace your dress!"

She then went to her bridal chest, opened it and took out the dress she had worn on the day of her marriage to Petrus Leonis.

Hannah Naemi, at last becoming aware of her intention: "Oh Miriam, spare your blind child! Wait for your father, and ask counsel of him!"

Miriam: "I am not waiting for my father, I am waiting for my son!"
Again: "Daughter, unlace your dress!"

Then Hannah Naemi clasped Trophäea to her, as though to protect her with her feeble old arms.

Hannah Naemi: "Oh Miriam, we poor, weak women!"

All at once Trophäea in the arms of Hannah Naemi, like one who begins talking in her sleep:

"Mother, here I am!"

Hannah Naemi: "Trophäea, for years you have resisted your mother, resist her now, for this one hour!"

Trophäea again: "Mother, here I am!" Suddenly, stretching out her arms from under the arms of Hannah Naemi, clear and strong like the voice of Miriam: "Mother, mother, here I am!"

Then Miriam drew her daughter into her arms and kissed her on the mouth and forehead.

Miriam: "Today you have become my child for the second time! The Lord has allowed me to become a mother in my old age!"

But just as Trophäea was obediently beginning to unlace her dress, she pulled her hands away.

Miriam: "Let be, daughter; it is for me, your mother, to wait on you on the day of your glory!"

And so Miriam took off Trophäea's dress for her, and clothed her in her own bridal robe.

Now as soon as Trophäea felt on her limbs the heavy purple silk she had so often fingered with such tender awe, she began to tremble, so greatly was she overcome at the thought that she was now actually going to wear this dress.

Trophäea: "Oh Mother, what are you doing? Why are you putting this dress on me? The Lord did not intend it for me!"

Miriam: "It is because you know this, that you may wear it."

Then Miriam put round her neck and on her wrists and fingers the chains and rings of her nuptial ornaments, and at each single piece Trophäea said in a low, humble voice: "The Lord did not intend it for me." And each time, Miriam replied: "It is because you know this, that you may wear it." Finally Miriam raised the crown to place it on Trophäea's head; but now Trophäea no longer said: "The Lord did not intend it for me," but she merely bent her head lower, for she could no longer speak.

THE Jews of Rome relate:
Miriam, when she had finished dressing Trophäea: "You are beautiful, O maiden, but your bloom is over; you are arrayed in finery, but your finery is faded. You are blind, for your people has wept much; you are forsaken, for your people has suffered much." Then: "Receive your mother's blessing!"

When Hannah Naemi heard these words, she could contain herself no longer, but rushed out into the street to fetch her brother, in order that he might put a stop to Miriam's mad project. In the meanwhile Miriam pronounced her blessing over Trophäea.

And Miriam blessed her daughter with the blessing of Aaron: "May the Lord bless thee and shield thee! May the Lord let His countenance shine upon thee and be merciful to thee! May the Lord raise His countenance over thee and give thee peace!"

Trophäea: "The Lord is over me, the Lord is with me!"

And so Miriam's daughter went to the house of Petrus Leonis clad in the same bridal dress in which her mother had once walked out of it into her martyrdom.

THE Canticle of Canticles, Chapter I (Trophäea, on entering the Pier Leone palace):

> "Let him kiss me with the kiss of his mouth,
> For his love is better than wine!
> Draw me, I will run after thee…
> We will be glad and rejoice in thee!

I am black, but beautiful, O ye daughters of Jerusalem,
As the tents of Cedar,
As the curtains of Solomon...."

The Canticle of Canticles, Chapter II (Trophäea, on entering the
Pier Leone palace):

"For the winter is now past, the rain is over and gone,
The flowers have appeared in our land: the time of pruning is come:
the voice of the turtle is heard in our land."

The Canticle of Canticles, Chapter VIII (Trophäea on entering the
Pier Leone palace):

"Oh, that I could find thee, my brother, who lay upon my mother's
breasts!
Oh, that I might kiss thee, and no man despise me!
I would bring thee into my mother's house, and I would give thee a
cup of spiced wine, and new wine of my pomegranates."

TROPHÄEA in the Pier Leone palace.

This is the legend which circulates among the people:

When Petrus Leonis lay dying, his dead wife, the beautiful Miriam,
who had left him on the day of his baptism, was seen returning to the
palace, arrayed in her bridal dress, and with the crown, which she had
then carried in her hands, once more upon her head, dress and crown
both faded after so many years, but clearly recognizable: it was thus that
the guards in the court below saw her, and also some of the servants in
the corridors at the back of the house, as she mounted the staircase leading to her old apartment, whence one passes between two red curtains
into the sumptuous chamber containing the marriage bed on which she
had formerly reposed with her husband.

TROPHÄEA in the Pier Leone palace.

As she came forward from behind the hangings, she looked so like her mother that Cardinal Pier Leone recognized her at once; for while he was legate in France they had shown him the statue in the Cathedral of Chartres, which is called "the Queen of Juda" and was carved in the likeness of Miriam, the Beautiful.

Profoundly moved and like one in a stupor: "It is my mother's face! It is truly my own mother that I see before me!" At the same time he told himself quite clearly that this woman who was advancing towards him could not possibly be she, as he judged her to be no older than himself. Besides he had always been told that his mother had died in giving him birth.

Meanwhile, Trophäea did not know that she had arrived: she only felt how the crown on her head rocked a little, and the chains and rings on her breast jingled more violently, as her heart quickened its beats at the thought that she must now soon be there. Led by the hand of the old Rachel, she advanced very cautiously and, so to speak, gropingly, as one walks when one is blind, but at the same time as if she were gliding through the air and no longer felt the earth beneath her feet for very joy. The Cardinal beheld the amazing apparition move past him and approach the bed of the dying man, but it did not enter his head to address it, so utterly was he taken aback and overcome by its presence. It was not until it stood close by the bed that he came to himself.

Cardinal Pier Leone springing up:

"Away, young woman, leave this dying man, you cannot be my mother."

Trophäea let go of Rachel's hand and went up to him. The Cardinal saw something take place in her countenance that struck him as far more wonderful even than her apparition.

Recoiling a step: "Who are you?"

Trophäea: "Your blind sister."

The Cardinal (recoiling another step; it seemed to him as though the anguish he had been through just now was assailing him in another form at once more poignant and more inevitable): "What do you want? Whom do you seek?"

Trophäea: "You, my brother."

The Cardinal (beside himself): "Who gives you the right to force your way in here?"

Trophäea (unruffled): "Your people Israel, that sends me." Falling on her knees: "My brother, listen to the voice of the Lord your God. Renounce the false glory that blinded your father! Humble yourself and return to your poor mother and your blind sister!"

Then the Cardinal felt again as if a flash of lightning flared up within him.

In the depths of his soul: "It is not Israel that sends her to me, but—Christ!"

At the same moment the first blows of the Frangipani crashed upon the doors of the room.

TROPHÄEA, when the doors fell in.

She did not know what was happening, but in her heart were these words: "Nothing more can happen, for I have touched my brother's heart." A moment later she felt him seize her hand and drag her away. Then a door closed and she was alone.

FROM the archives of our golden city of Rome.

In what we are now going to relate, there is not, as might so easily be supposed, a shadow of exaggeration, nor the smallest piece of invention, although those of us who were assembled that day in the vestibule of the palace could never afterwards understand how it all happened. For the two doors of the bed-chamber which Cardinal Pier Leone had carefully bolted, were really and truly forced open by the Frangipani before our very eyes, that is to say, they were broken in just as the doors of Sancta Maria in Palara had previously been; not, it is true, like the latter, under the protection of a crowd of riders and armed men engaged for the purpose, but by a handful of daring spirits, who entered the hall so impudently and with such an air of unconcern, that we all of us thought they were merely some men of the palace who had been charged by the Pier Leoni to effect some repairs to the doors. (But there is further to be said in our excuse that we were still utterly bewildered by what had passed at the death-bed of Petrus Leonis.) Moreover, everything happened so quickly that it was over, so to speak, before it had properly begun. Afterwards, when the doors lay splintered in pieces on either side, we all beheld for the space of a moment the beautiful Miriam, the dead wife, beside the bed of her dying husband, just as we have previously described her, arrayed in the purple-red bridal dress she wore the day she had walked out of the palace, the crown she had then carried in her hands once more upon her head, both crown and dress, together with the gold of the chains and rings attached thereto, tarnished with the years, as when candles burn in the night mist, but everything and she herself as well, clearly recognizable as many of us still remember to have seen her in her life-time. And thus we were so stupefied by this astonishing vision that we forgot about the shattered doors, until the men of the Pier Leoni forced their way into the room to seize the intruders. These retreated under cover of their weapons to the back of the apartment, and amidst their swords—so it seemed to us—the beautiful Miriam, the dead wife, vanished from our sight. Then the combatants also disappeared, passing behind the red curtains into the interior of the palace. There they continued their fighting, and the din of the tumult was heard for hours afterwards along all the corridors. Hence it is that we say in Rome to this day: "The death of Petrus Leonis was not tolled with bells but with swords."

Trophäea in the Pier Leone palace.

She was still obsessed by this sole thought: I have touched my brother's heart, I have fulfilled the will of the Lord—what can happen to me? This thought made her happier than she had been at any time since the days of her childhood. It did not occur to her that she was alone and blind in a large, unknown palace; this fact only forced itself on her consciousness when the shouts of the combatants drew near. At first she waited a moment expecting Rachel or her brother to come back and fetch her. But no one came: she felt nothing around her save the cold, confined air that ascends from the secluded passages of old seignorial mansions.

Groping along the walls, but still without fear, almost joking with herself: "If I had been the prudent Pagan Ariadne, I would have brought a thread with me, when I entered this big, strange house—"

Meanwhile, the noise of the swords and the shouting of the combatants came nearer and nearer.

Trophäea: "My thread is the will of the Lord, who sent me to this house. Let Him lead me whithersoever He will—"

And so the Lord led Trophäea to the chapel of the palace, against the walls of which she had knocked as a child, when she replied to the Jewish woman: "My game is called: going into the house of Petrus Leonis."

THE chronicle relates:

Now it happened that on this particular night there stood in the chapel the Infant Jesus of the church of Sancta Maria on the Capitol, which we call: the Infant Jesus of Rome.

First, we will ask the Infant's blessing.

Then we will relate the following:

Of the church of Sancta Maria on the Capitol it is said: "*Ubi est ara filii Dei*," for it stands on the spot where for the first time in our city of Rome, the Infant Jesus was beheld in the arms of the Most Blessed Virgin Mary, in the days, that is to say, of the Emperor Octavian who ruled over our Pagan forefathers long before the holy apostles Peter and Paul announced the Savior to us.

Now we will ask the Infant's blessing for the second time (for we always do this several times, whenever we speak of this image).

CONTINUING our narrative:

This Pagan Emperor Octavian summoned the Sibyl from the grottoes of the Tiber to the temple which stands on the Capitoline hill in our city of Rome. There he asked her: whether, as lord of the whole universe, he was worthy to receive divine honors and sacrifices such as the people desired to offer him.

The Sibyl gave him this answer: "From heaven descends the King of the ages! Behold the virgin who bears the Lord of the world!"

At the same moment the clouds opened and the emperor beheld an altar borne by the splendor of thousands of radiant angels, and throned on it Mary the Mother of God with the Infant Jesus.

Now for the third time we will ask the Infant to bless us: may the Infant Jesus of Rome bless us and protect us all!

AGAIN continuing our narrative:

And that is why we have kept from ancient days at the exact spot where this happened, namely in the church of Sancta Maria on the Capitol, an image of the Infant Jesus made of a precious wood and swaddled in the finest linen and silkiest silk. The Infant wears on its hands as many rings as it has fingers, these having been dedicated to it by the young mothers of our city of Rome. On Christmas Eve we lay the Infant in a golden crib, and our own children come and sing their cradle-songs before it. Then from the country around Rome, shepherds come into the city, like the shepherds of Bethlehem, piping on their flutes and shawms all kinds of sweet airs. But during the year we like to take the Infant to our sick and dying that they may touch it and be cured, be it here below or beyond in eternal life. And so it was that on this day the Infant had been brought to the Pier Leone palace, that it might give succour to the master of the house on his death-bed; but when they wanted to take it into him, the doors were already shut, and the priests had therefore carried it to the chapel, that it might repose there until they came to take it away again. And there it lay this night at the foot of the cross on the altar.

TROPHÄEA in the chapel of the palace:

As she entered she felt at once the overpowering yet sweet stillness that reigned in the place. Here the air itself was no longer cold and lifeless as in the labyrinth of shut-in passages out of which she had come, but it seemed to her that she was now in a lofty room in which warm fragrance breathed, as if sweet spices had been burnt there.

Trophäea to herself: "It is good to be here. I should like to remain here and see what happens to me."

She closed the door behind her, and advanced full of confidence; and at every step the mysterious feeling of well-being the live stillness of the place created in her, seemed to increase.

Trophäea again: "It is good to be here. It feels here as if the angels of the Lord had made it their home. I should like to remain here."

And so, groping her way in the manner of the blind, she traversed the whole chapel, until, passing between the marble stalls of the choir she felt a small step at her feet.

Trophäea: "I will rest on this step. How happy I feel here!"

And she sat herself down. But when she tried to rest, the weight of the crown began to press on her head, and she took it off. In so doing she knocked her arm against a table which stood close to the step.

Trophäea: "It is my mother's crown, it is the crown of my own life— it shall not lie on the bare ground!"

She stood up and tenderly placed the crown on the table. Then she sat down again on the step.

In the complete stillness that now lay about her, the voice of her joy again made itself heard in her heart: "I felt how I touched my brother's heart! I have fulfilled the will of the Lord! What more can happen to me? I will thank the Lord for all he has given me to do."

TROPHÄEA before the altar of the chapel:

> "The Lord ruleth me: and I shall want nothing, He hath set me in
>   a place of pasture.
> He hath brought me up on the water of refreshment:
> He hath converted my soul.
> He hath led me on the paths of justice for his own name's sake.

For though I should walk in the midst of the shadow of death, I
    will fear no evils for thou art with me—
And thy mercy will follow me all the days of my life.
And I shall dwell in the house of the Lord unto length of days."

Trophäea before the altar of the chapel:

"Praise the Lord, Oh my soul!
In my life I will praise the Lord!
I will sing to my God as long as I shall be!
The Lord giveth food to the hungry:
The Lord looseth them that are fettered:
The Lord enlighteneth the blind:
The Lord lifteth up them that are cast down:
The Lord keepeth the strangers:
He will support the fatherless and the widow.
The Lord shall reign forever: thy God, oh Sion, unto generation
    and generation."

Trophäea before the altar of the chapel:

"Give praise to the Lord, for He is good, for his mercy endureth
    for ever!
I shall not die, but live: and shall declare the works of the Lord.
This is the day which the Lord has made!
Let us be glad and rejoice therein.
Blessed be he that cometh in the name of the Lord!
O praise ye the Lord, for he is good: for his mercy endureth
    forever."

And then Trophäea chanted before the altar of the chapel all the
psalms and hymns of King David and could not leave off. But the longer
she prayed, the more it seemed to her that she was not praying alone,

but that there was someone else in the room praying with her or for her in her stead.

Trophäea: "Who is there? Who is in this room praying with me? Who is it whose heart is so close to mine? Alas, if I could only see and know where I am!"

And then Trophäea began to feel around her with her hands, trying to find out who it was that seemed so near her.

But the Lord, who had previously guided Trophäea's steps to the chapel, now guided her hand also, so that in feeling over the altar, she did not touch the hostile Christian Sign of the Cross, which would have horrified her, but the Infant Jesus.

TROPHÄEA in the chapel of the palace:

Trophäea: "I feel the image of a little child in my hands: swaddled in linen, with small, fragile limbs, like the limbs of infants that lie before young mothers in the cradle."

At the same time she was conscious of a strange fear in her heart. (This was due, she supposed, to the fact that the voices of the little children in front of the Rabbi's house had always caused her such irritation and made her feel so sad.)

Trophäea: "But I have surrendered my will to God! Am I not myself become like a little child before Him, very small and very humble? How then can I still fret my heart out, because I have no child? Why should I be frightened at the image of this Infant?"

Then, her serenity restored, she took the Infant in her arms, as though to show God that her will was now completely at one with His....

This happened in the early hours of the third Sunday before the Passion of Our Lord Jesus Christ, when they intone the Introit of Holy Mass with the words: "*Laetare Jerusalem!*"

But these are the very words which, at her mother's command, Trophäea had recited on the evening when with the women of the Jews she listened on the banks of the Tiber for the sound of the holy trumpet, just before she ran into the midst of the hostile troop of horsemen.

FROM the archives of our golden city of Rome.

Meanwhile, outside the chapel, the Frangipani and their little hand-ful of men still held together and stood their ground defiantly, for the corridors in that part of the Pier Leone palace are very narrow, and not more than three or four men can pass abreast there. Consequently the far greater numbers of the Pier Leoni availed them little; only a few of their men could engage at a time, and these were quickly repulsed each time by the bold Frangipani. While the fighting was still going on Petrus Leonis passed away, and out of respect for the dead man the Pier Leoni discontinued the combat. They offered the Frangipani a free retreat if they agreed to withdraw quietly, but the latter would not listen to them.

Among themselves: "We care nothing about a free retreat; we are here because of the dead wife, Miriam, in whom we absolutely refuse to believe; on the contrary we believe that it was a living Jewish maiden we saw just now at the bedside of Petrus Leonis, and later in these cor-ridors. We will not withdraw from here, therefore, until we have cleared this matter up, for we may well discover something that it will profit us to know. Let us then seize the opportunity, now that the Pier Leoni are busy with their corpses, and search the place thoroughly." (Moving towards the chapel.)

TROPHÄEA in the chapel:

Several hours had now passed, and she waited in vain for her brother to come and fetch her.

Trophäea: "Yet I felt that I touched his heart! Perhaps I did not touch it deeply enough? Or can a heart that is touched forget again?"

And gradually she began to grow uneasy, as if her joy had to descend from a high mountain into a deep valley.

TROPHÄEA in the chapel:

It was now no longer King David's hymns of praise that she chanted, but his anxious cries for help.

TROPHÄEA:

"Lord, incline thy ear unto me and save me.
Deliver me, for my heart is troubled within me.
In thee, O Lord, I have hoped: let me never be put to confusion.
Deliver me in Thy justice and rescue me.
Have mercy on me, O Lord, for I am weak.
Hear me, O Lord, for my bones are troubled, and my soul is
   troubled exceedingly: but thou, O Lord, how long?"

TROPHÄEA in the chapel:
"I have prayed with such fervor! Can it really be then that the Lord
has forsaken his poor blind child?"

TROPHÄEA in the chapel:
"Can it be, too, that my mother's faith is confounded? Can it be that
her whole life's hope is vain?"
   Suddenly she seemed to become clearly aware of this certitude: "The
Lord will not send you your brother! The Lord will not deliver you from
your forsakenness, but He will be forsaken with you!"
   Trophäea: "What a strange place I am in! What extraordinary ideas
come to me here! How can the Almighty God be forsaken and helpless?
Such an idea never entered my head before."
   Again it seemed to her as if there was someone else in the room, and
that he was whispering to her. And she began to feel about her as before.
This time her hand touched the cross on the altar, but she was not aware
of it, her mind being conscious only of the infant.
   Again she seemed to hear the unknown voice at her side: "God will
not take charge of His poor blind child, but He Himself will become a
weak child with her."
   This so moved her, that she bent over the Infant and kissed it.
   And it was at that moment that the Frangipani burst in and carried
her off.

XI

FROM the notes of the Cardinal-Bishop Petrus of Portus: As I became advanced in years, and my desire to be with Christ increased, I often besought Him in my prayers to take me home to Him, but now that I have reached an extreme old age, and my desire to depart this life knows no bounds, I merely pray that the will of Jesus Christ, our King, may be accomplished at all times and in all places, and also as regards the duration of my poor life; be it to my joy or sorrow. And so, too, in praying for Holy Church at this hour, I merely pray that His will be done.

But for many days now we have been waiting for the moment when it will please our dying Father, Pope Honorius, in accordance with the custom among the successors of St. Peter, to give us his counsel touching the election of our future master, in order that he may continue for the duration of his mortal life to assist us with the wisdom's light of his holy office, which light—as we well know—can be replaced by no other. So far, however, our Holy Father has kept silence. Accordingly, as the oldest among our brothers, I presented myself before Pope Honorius, to question him frankly on the subject.

He lay on his couch, very small and pitiful; his tall and once so muscular frame all bent and shriveled, the big bones in his cheeks and hands protruding like sharp points, his disproportionately high forehead looking as if it was about to take flight from the tiny face beneath; the face itself finely chiseled and of the paleness of wax, as in persons of noble birth (he himself, however, came of peasant stock). I related to him (for this seemed to me, after all that had happened, a suitable disguise for my question), what Pope Callixtus had formerly said to me about our brother, Pier Leone, when he felt his end approaching. For although our canons forbid us, so long as our Sovereign Pontiff still breathes, to enter into any discussion among ourselves regarding the person of the next Pope, there was one name uppermost in the minds of many of us, and we can well say that we often abstained from mentioning it to each other.

I soon perceived, however, that our Holy Father Honorius no longer understood me, so far away had his shining eyes strayed from me, as though his fleeing brow were the symbol of his escaping thoughts. I did not fail to inform our brothers of this.

Meanwhile rumors are chasing each other like wild horses through all the streets of the city.

FROM the notes of the Cardinal-Bishop Petrus of Portus:

We do not know yet what has actually happened, for our brother Heimericus keeps an imperturbable silence amid the storm of all these voices, so that one might think he regarded them as no concern of ours.

The two Frangipani sent us word that in the chapel of the Pier Leone palace they had seized a young Jewish woman, who, to all appearances, was on the point of carrying away the Infant Jesus of Sancta Maria on the Capitol, it being a notorious fact that the Jews frequently laid violent hands on the holy images of the Christians, and even on the consecrated hosts, bearing them off to their synagogues, where they exposed them to the most horrible indignities. If our brother Heimericus was agreeable, they proposed to hand over the young woman to him, in order that he might question her himself as to how she came to be in the palace. In their opinion it was of some importance that Holy Church should be duly informed of everything that had taken place at the death-bed of Petrus Leonis.

To this our brother Heimericus replied: Since the young Jewish woman had been seized in the Pier Leone palace, the matter concerned the Pier Leoni and not him. They would do well then to take her back to the place where they had found her, and leave her to be examined there; that would be the best way of finding out the reason of her presence in the palace and what she was doing there.

THE Cardinal-Bishop of Portus once more:

The Frangipani sent a second message to our brother Heimericus to inform him that they had themselves examined the young Jewish woman: she declared that she was own sister to Cardinal Pier Leone, and had been brought up in Judaism, and that she had been summoned to the death-bed of Petrus Leonis by the Cardinal himself. They felt bound in conscience to report to Holy Church such extraordinary revelations.

To this our brother Heimericus, with undisturbed countenance: He was pleasantly surprised to see that the Frangipani had the interests of Holy Church so much at heart; he could only repeat, however, that if the woman was the Cardinal's sister, the whole affair was the latter's concern and not his. Would they please return their captive to the Pier Leone palace.

We know only too well, however, that the Frangipani would like to use this Jewess they have seized to ruin our brother Pier Leone, and above all to exclude him from the papal election, for we have been informed that they are spreading the report on all sides that the Pier Leoni were only baptized for form's sake, and that in reality they are still Jews, like the old Rachel, of whom this is known in all Rome. And so it surprises us to see them now suddenly posing as the protectors of Christendom.

But speaking for ourselves, we are of the opinion that the hour is now come when our brother Pier Leone must answer the question put to him by our Holy Father Paschal. Thus what we are waiting for now, is not so much to see what these Frangipani will do next, as to see what our brother Pier Leone will do.

Meanwhile the people are raising a clamor on all sides on account of the disappearance of the Infant Jesus of Sancta Maria, which the Frangipani are believed to have transferred to their palace at the same time that

they captured the Jewish woman. Our brother Heimericus has therefore
ordered the Frangipani to restore the image at once and with becoming
reverence to the church to which it belongs.

FROM the archives of our golden city of Rome.

We have conversed with a handmaid from the house of the Frangipani, of the name of Trulla. And she related the following:

At that time we said at the castle: "Our masters are not so fair of hair
and skin as they used to be, but it is with them as when a cloud comes
over the city of Rome and the yellow and white marble on the Palatine
becomes discolored. Also they do not seem to us to be quite as wild as
formerly, but they have become more malicious. And so many of us say:
Bah, our masters are getting older, that is all! But we have noticed this
change in them ever since the day when Bishop Lambert of Ostia, and
not Cardinal Pier Leone, was elected Pope, for from that day they both
do everything our mistress Jacoba tells them to do. This does not make
for their peace of mind, on the contrary it upsets them; for people like
them can do a number of things that other folk shrink from, without it
weighing on their conscience, but once they begin to lie, gall enters their
blood and poisons their whole system. I think, however, they know themselves that in clamoring so loudly for the pious Bishop Lambert they
played into the hands of Petrus Leonis, of whom many now say that he
became a Christian only to make his fortune in this world. For although
our masters always take the advice of our mistress Jacoba, they are not
a bit grateful to her on that account, but even our young master Leo
now often treats her harshly. And in consequence she herself is becoming
more ill-tempered every day, so that I pity her from my heart. Were I a
rich lady, I would buy a lamp and I would hang it up before the image of
the merciful Mother of God, that it might burn there for the poor heart
of our mistress, for many injustices had that heart to suffer in the days
when it pined for love of our master Cencius. But a person cannot suffer
great injustice without harm to himself, unless he truly loves Christ and
His Blessed Mother, otherwise it is more than his strength can bear."

Thus spoke Trulla, the poor handmaid, who herself had to suffer many an injustice in the course of her life.

THE handmaid Trulla from the house of the Frangipani.

She continued her narrative:

In those days our mistress made us procure her a sorceress, as she wanted to consult one about the forthcoming papal election and about the future of her family. Accordingly, some of us searched the streets where these women are to be found, and there the old Rachel presented herself to us. And so this woman came into the castle of our masters. (Today, however, we no longer believe that Rachel was a sorceress, but we are convinced that she came to us for the same reason that she had previously gone to Miriam.)

We conducted her to a little side room near the door, for we were afraid that if our master Cencius caught sight of her, he would strangle her on the spot. We then called our mistress.

She entered, holding our young master Leo affectionately by the hand, for she still liked to pretend that the same cordial relations existed between them as before, although he had become so harsh and unfriendly towards her.

Then extending her beautiful hand to Rachel (for she thought she would question her about her own destiny first): "Well, what do you know about me, old Jewess?"

Rachel, examining her hand, with concealed sarcasm: "That you once offered your hand to one of the circumcised, Lady!"

At these words our master Leo sprang at the old woman's throat, but our mistress tore him away.

Our mistress: "What she tells me, Leo, is very valuable, can't you understand?"

She then rewarded the old woman and dismissed her.

Afterwards to our masters: "Do you not see how excellently it all fits in: the death of Petrus Leonis, the Jewish woman you seized in the chapel, and now what this old witch has just said? True enough, you cannot reach the cardinals, for they will not allow us to speak evil of any man, but you can reach the people. For although they stick to the gold purses of the Pier Leoni like burrs, they are always ready to listen to a piece of scandal if it is shouted loud enough."

She then gave them this advice: Let them obey the Chancellor's command, and thus compel the Cardinal to recognize his Jewish sister publicly prior to the conclave. It would be the very best thing that could happen, if, on the eve of the papal election, everyone were again reminded of the strange events that took place at the death-bed of Petrus Leonis.

They finally decided to dispatch a herald, who should ride through the streets of the city in broad daylight and with as much noise as possible to the Pier Leone palace, and ask by sound of trumpet whether the Cardinal was coming to fetch his Jewish sister whom they had caught in the act of carrying off the Infant Jesus, or where did he wish her to be taken? Meanwhile the Jewess herself and the Infant Jesus were both being kept as hostages, since they did not know but what they might still have to make use of them. With these instructions the herald rode off to Cardinal Pier Leone.

CARDINAL Pier Leone.

Meanwhile in the chapel of the Pier Leone palace, Trophäea's bridal crown still lay on the altar at the foot of the cross, where Trophäea had placed it when she removed it from her head. Now, however, stretched on a bier in front of the altar, lay the dead body of Petrus Leonis, with the golden senatorial mitre, which in his death agony he had so violently shaken off, once again upon his head, and gorgeously arrayed in a purple dalmatic like the corpse of a great prince, but as forsaken as the corpse of the wretchedest beggar or malefactor. For the people of the palace had not yet recovered from the shock of his terrifying end, and they could hardly wait for the moment to arrive when the corpse should be removed from the house. Donna Bona, on the other hand, and her children, were afraid of the dead wife, Miriam, who had been seen at the death-bed of their husband and father. Thus Cardinal Pier Leone remained hour after hour alone with the corpse. But outside the door of the chapel the servants said to each other: "The son wishes to commune undisturbed with his dead father for the last time." In this way they excused themselves in their own eyes for not wanting to pray by the dead body of their master. Cardinal Pier Leone alone with his dead father.

He was not looking at him, however, but his eyes were fixed on the bridal crown beneath the cross on the altar; it seemed to him as it lay there that it was praying equally for him and to him.

Cardinal Pier Leone continuing his train of thought, interrupted at his father's death-bed: "No, it is not Israel that sends you, but Christ—" Glancing at the mitre of the dead man (it now rested immovable on the inert head, but the large, white mouth still stood half open, as if the frozen cry, "my people Israel," held the lips apart).

"Father, I cannot relieve you of this mitre; its very dust will burden your dust even in the grave! And yet you were an honest man: you paid your debt loyally, yes, you paid it many times over."

Bending lower over the dead man: But it was no longer the great, the mighty Consul and Senator of the Romans that lay before him, but his eyes beheld the countenance of an old, sad and much tormented man, on which were engraven neither the triumphs and victories of his life, nor the dizzy figures of his gold bezants, but on it stood recorded an infinity of humiliations great and small, one beside the other, as if registered on a roll of patient, silent and enduring parchment. The Cardinal recognized them all again, one after the other, as though he were reading the secret record of his own life.

Cardinal Pier Leone: "And all this—was in reality then the call of Christ? Our despised people the Cross we fled from? the Cross that pursued us?"

Turning again to the crown that lay on the altar beseeching him: "So the Cross and Love are one? Oh, Jesus Christ, how cunning are Thy ways, when it is a question of winning a soul!"

CARDINAL Pier Leone writing this letter in his inmost soul:

"...And this is why I beg of you, reverend and dear Brothers, to banish henceforward, once and for all, all the anxiety which, as I know full well, Holy Church has suffered on my account since the death of Pope Callixtus. For my ambitions are not concerned with the matter about which that anxiety exists, but I regard myself as called by Christ to devote myself from now on with a special love to the cause of my brothers and sisters of the house of Israel, that they may be united to Christ or—if such be not God's will—that, acting as their spokesman, I may labor on their behalf among the Christians, to the end that they may live in peace and without injury among us. But I would ask you, my brothers, to join with me in a petition to our future Sovereign Pontiff and Father whom you are about to choose under the guidance of the Holy Spirit, that he may grant me His apostolic blessing in this my mission—"

To himself, laying his pen aside as it were: "And so I shall not be Pope, but I shall henceforth be a Christian."

CARDINAL Pier Leone.

Suddenly in his inner self—flashing up like the perceptions that came to him at the bedside of his dying father, though not like them rising abruptly from the depths of hidden worlds, but as if the keen clarity of his mind flashed its light into the domain of his soul—these words: "And yet, if I am a Christian, I can also be Pope! Yes, they will count this very letter as a merit in me; with it I will stifle the rumors that threaten me; with it I will triumph over all my enemies! And if I triumph, well, I can also protect!"

At that moment, the herald of the Frangipani arrived before the castle.

CARDINAL Pier Leone.

As he hurried out of the chapel to put a stop to the unseemly hubbub that was going on outside the house of his dead father (for a large crowd of people had followed the herald through the streets), his sister Tullia came rushing towards him with such precipitation that her long black veil flapped about her face.

Cardinal Pier Leone angrily: "Why are you rushing about like this, Tullia? Have you forgotten our dead father in the chapel?"

Tullia Pier Leone (they were already saying in Sicily: there are times when our princess hardly seems in her right mind, she gets such strange fancies into her head), trembling: "Forgive me, brother! I had such a bad dream last night: I dreamed that I was again at the house of the Frangipani, but they did not dance with me, they kept me prisoner."

The Cardinal again angrily: "What does this dream matter, Tullia? Are you not the wife of Prince Roger? Say the words: Sicily and Apulia, before going to sleep."

Tullia, still trembling: "Brother, the dream has come true: the herald of the Frangipani is at the gate and says I stole the Infant Jesus!" Bursting into tears: "Oh, help me!"

The Cardinal in the depths of his soul: "So it is not: triumph over your enemies, but rather: deliver yourself into their hands? Oh, Jesus Christ, now Thou art not cunning, but terrible!"

FROM the notes of the Cardinal-Bishop Petrus of Portus.

The Frangipani sent a message to our brother Heimericus saying that they had obeyed his orders and had offered to hand over their captive Jewess to Cardinal Pier Leone; he, however, had rejected their offer and refused admittance to their herald.

Whereupon our brother Heimericus inquired whether they had also obeyed his second order and returned the sacred image of the Infant Jesus to Sancta Maria. He commanded them to do this without further delay; as regards the young Jewish woman, however, they were to hand her over to the Jew, Nathan ben Jechiel. The latter had come to us in the meantime to plead for his granddaughter, imploring us with many tears to have her restored to him, and at the same time giving us convincing proof that she could not possibly have carried off the image, as she was blind.

For myself I could see that our brother Heimericus was annoyed at the message of the Frangipani, for I know well what it means when the two grey falcons under his brow flap their wings.

Shortly afterwards the Frangipani delivered up both the Jewess and the image; but they did so in their own fashion.

FROM the archives of our golden city of Rome.

We also inquired of the handmaid, Trulla, whether she could give us any information as to what happened to Trophäea during her confinement in the house of the Frangipani. She could tell us very little, however, and thus already at this point there falls the veil of Our Lady, the most blessed and most dolorous Virgin Mary, under which—as we believe—Trophäea vanished from our midst. And so we will speak no more of her save to relate her end.

THE handmaid Trulla from the house of the Frangipani:

Meanwhile, however, the people were becoming more and more enraged on account of the Infant Jesus of Sancta Maria which our masters kept locked up in our house together with the Jewess in order to prove the evil intentions of the latter in regard to it. And at last the mob made a rush for the castle of our masters, where amid threats and shouts of abuse they voiced their opinion: that if the Pier Leoni were, as was said, secretly Jews, they, the Frangipani, were manifest Pagans, ravishers of the Infant Son of God; that the crime of the captive Jewess had yet to be proved, whereas the crime of the Frangipani was clear as daylight. They demanded the immediate return of the sacred image to Sancta Maria in accordance with the Cardinal-Chancellor's command, otherwise they would do to the Frangipane castle what the French knights had done.

In reply our masters ordered the archers to shoot their arrows among the crowd; whereupon it dispersed with loud cries and made for the Lateran Palace in order to complain to Cardinal Heimericus of the conduct of our masters.

Soon afterwards, our mistress Jacoba again spoke to these: "I am going to propose to you an even better plan than the first. You will see how the people can be made to believe the guilt of this Jewess; after which they will surely want to question Cardinal Pier Leone publicly about his sister!"

She then sent me away and had a talk with her cousins. Soon afterwards our masters came into the large hall and demanded wine. They then returned to their rooms, bolted the doors and went to bed.

THE handmaid Trulla from the house of the Frangipani.

Meanwhile I went once again to our small, dusty chapel, where the Holy Infant Jesus had been deposited—or rather, I should say, imprisoned, for that is how it seemed to me. It lay on the bare, deserted altar more miserable than once in the crib at Bethlehem, and every day before going to bed I asked its pardon in my prayers for the dishonor done to it.

When I entered that evening, the Infant had gone.

I hurried out and ran to inform my mistress; for I said to myself: perhaps someone from among the people has secretly carried the image away or maybe (trembling in my soul) it has departed from this godless house of its own accord. But my mistress was not in her room. So I ran breathless to the door of our masters; but I could not make them hear, they were lying down in a heavy stupor like full wine-flagons. I then went up to the maids' quarters, where I found a young girl still sitting up.

She told me that she had just seen our mistress and another woman slip out by the postern-gate behind the temple of the Romans, and that if I hurried I could easily catch them up.

Down I ran to the postern; it stood half open, as one leaves a gate when one intends to return almost at once. Then on into the narrow lane; it was white with the shimmer of stars; these were falling on all sides like drops of milk upon the earth. (Never before had such a rain of stars been seen.)

On turning the corner where, through the Arch of the Seven-branched Candlestick, the road issues on to the ancient Forum of the Romans—tonight, however, there were no lights of the Pagan spirits to be seen in the Forum, but only the falling of this gentle milk of heaven—I perceived a bare ten paces in front of me my mistress standing under the Arch with the woman of whom the girl had spoken. (But I saw at once that it was the captive Jewess.) My mistress placed a bundle in the other's arms; at that moment another milk-white star dropped to earth, and I recognized in the bundle the little Infant Jesus of Sancta Maria. My mistress then returned alone.

Immediately the lights of the Pagans, like little red frogs leaping from the earth, sprang up on all sides before the path of my mistress.

I hastily slipped with my bare feet behind a column, until my mistress and the little red frogs had happily passed me. Meanwhile the Jewess remained standing under the Arch.

I said to myself: one can see that she is blind, for no child of Israel has ever been known to stand under this Arch.

Suddenly I felt as if, for the sake of the mercy of Our Lord Jesus Christ, I must go up to her and say: "Maiden, give me the Infant, for my mistress is using it to destroy you and yours."

But I saw another woman already standing near the Jewess under the Arch. (I thought it was one of her own people.) This woman took her by the hand, and they went away together. But behind them the stars fell like a white curtain.

When I arrived back home, the whole palace was already in uproar: The captive Jewess had secretly escaped and taken the Infant Jesus with her; thus her wicked purpose was now clear to everybody. Then our men sprang to their horses and careered through the city after her, rousing the people from sleep on all sides, and making them join in the pursuit.

TROPHÄEA and the Strange Woman.

The Strange Woman: "I thank you, gentle maiden, for carrying this Infant!"

Trophäea (she thought that it was still Jacoba Frangipane at her side): "I will gladly carry it, Lady, if you will guide me, for I do not know where am."

The Strange Woman: "I know quite well where we are, for I have often been here with my Child before. But I am anxious that it should be taken back to its home by you."

Trophäea: "What, is the Infant yours? I thought it belonged to my brother's house."

The Strange Woman: "Yes, dear sister, it is mine."

Trophäea (she now realized that it was not Jacoba Frangipane she was addressing): "You say 'sister'; are you then one of us?"

The Strange Woman: "Truly I am one of you—can you not see?"

Trophäea: "I cannot see, for I am blind."

The Strange Woman: "In the place we are going to, a blind Pagan once learned to see." (She was alluding to the Emperor Octavian.)

They now ascended the steps leading to the Capitol.

The Strange Woman: "Now you will soon see, dear sister! But first of all you yourself must be seen, for I do not want people to think ill of you."

And now they were at the steps of Sancta Maria.

But there was already a large crowd of people, who had been routed from their beds by the Frangipani, assembled there, filling the night-gloom of the church with their prayers and lamentations on account of the stolen Infant Jesus. (Among them were also several of the Frangipani.) One could hear their murmurs and plaints from afar.

The Strange Woman again: "In a moment you will see, dear sister!"

They now crossed the threshold of the church.

Suddenly a voice raised a loud cry as if before a miracle of God: "The Infant Jesus is returning! The Jewess herself is bringing it back!"

At these words, many felt as if their knees were giving way beneath them; but one man sprang forward in a frenzy of rage.

At the same moment Trophäea felt a strangely warm pain in her breast, as if all the blood of her heart were suddenly flowing over.

The Strange Woman close to her ear: "Now, my dearest sister, you see!"

Trophäea to the Strange Woman (Frangipane's sword in her heart): "I see…I see you and the Infant…on the altar of Heaven…"

FROM the archives of our golden city of Rome.

"What are we to say of this event? Did a miracle of divine illumination take place in respect of this Jewess? Did she, in order to bring us back the holy Infant Jesus, suffer martyrdom, and thereby, as the Doctors of our holy Church teach, receive the baptism of blood? Or does what has happened prove that since the Incarnation of Our Lord, even those who do not recognize Him are nevertheless drawn to Him, provided they are of good will and the love of God dwells in their hearts?" Thuswise did our priests discuss the matter among themselves. But we said to them: "Question and ponder to your hearts' content, for that is your office! But for us it is sufficient that this Jewess brought us back the holy Infant Jesus, like a servant and daughter of the Mother of God, and like Her with a sword in her heart. We therefore demand that she be buried in our Church."

Meanwhile, however, the Frangipani had hurriedly removed the body behind our backs, saying: "Let us take it to the Pier Leone palace; perhaps the dead woman will betray the Cardinal, since he shunned her when she was alive."

And so Trophäea was brought to the Pier Leone palace for the second time.

THE Pier Leone palace.

This is what the servants of the house have to tell.

That night the silver coffin of our master Petrus Leonis was closed down (it was afterwards placed in the stone sarcophagus which now lies in the basilica of St. Paul Outside-the-Walls); and so the blows of the hammer resounded through the length and breadth of the vast gloomy palace. But we were still too frightened to remain near the coffin of our dead master, even though the lid had now been put on; besides, it seemed to us that the work was proceeding all too slowly. The fact was that the master silversmith who had made the coffin had fallen ill, and they had sent for an old travelling apprentice from one of the inns. This man seemed to us very clumsy at his job.

When at last he had finished it, he said to us: would we please call our master the Cardinal, as he wished to receive his wage.

We: It was already long past bed-time, and our master had retired, could he not wait until the morning?

He: No, he could not, as he had to take the road again before daybreak.

We: Then he had better go himself to our master; we could not take it upon ourselves to rouse him at such an hour.

CARDINAL Pier Leone and the Silversmith.

(But we do not know whether the Cardinal was awake or dreaming.)

The Silversmith: "I have finished, Your Eminence. Your father's coffin is closed down, but before you pay me, you had better test the nails carefully once more, so that, if the dead man slips out again, no one can say afterwards that I did my work badly."

The Cardinal angrily: "How dare you presume to make such an unseemly jest?"

The Silversmith: "It is not an unseemly jest, Your Eminence, for every day the same people rise again whom we have previously buried."

The Cardinal, taken aback: "You seem to be a dialectician?"

The Silversmith: "Why should I not be a dialectician? In long years of wandering one meets with many experiences."

The Cardinal: "What is your name?"

The Silversmith: "Not one that you would care to hear. But what's in a name?"

The Cardinal eyed the stranger sharply: he was gray and decrepit, his nose hanging over his face like the curved bough of a withered tree over an old road.

Hesitatingly: "You are not, I think—a Christian?"

The Silversmith laughing: "A Christian? I do not know what a Christian is. If I knew that, I would have left this world long ago."

The Cardinal abruptly: "What does all this mean?"

The Silversmith: "All this means that it has been imposed upon me—let us say as a penance—to wander from land to land in search of a true Christian, but I have never found one. See how far I have wandered already!" (Shaking the dust from his shoes.)

The Cardinal (for it seemed to him that he must comport himself as a priest): "Then you cannot have searched properly. There are many charitable and saintly souls among the Christians."

The Silversmith: "So I have heard; but there do not exist nearly enough. Or perhaps it is part of my penance that I am never to meet the right man, but am doomed only to meet the like of what I am myself—let us say the Wandering Man; for the Christian, well—he is, I suppose, something more than a mere man?"

The Cardinal: "The Wandering Man? Hitherto I have heard only of the Wandering Jew!"

The Silversmith: "That is a false name." (Again shaking the dust from his feet.)

Suddenly it seemed to the Cardinal as if all the roads of the world opened up before him.

Frozen with fear: "And what do you seek here, with me, sinister companion?"

The Silversmith: "Exactly what I seek everywhere, for you too have been baptized. But come outside with me; there we will both learn more clearly what we desire to know." (Moving towards the door.)

At that moment this was opened from outside.

Tullia Pier Leone on the threshold: "Oh my brother, my brother! Why did you not come to my help? The Frangipani have now killed me!"

XII

———————◆———————

THE Jews of Rome relate: It was now the time when our people prepare for the Feast of the Passover, which we call "the Feast of our deliverance from the land of Egypt." Accordingly in the house of Rabbi Nathan ben Jechiel also, they set about baking the unleavened bread. Hannah Naemi, however, could not bake, for she was afraid her tears might fall into the paste. So Miriam baked the unleavened bread alone. The reason was that Miriam did not, like Hannah Naemi, await Trophäea's return with tears and trembling, but she was filled with a vain confidence, so that her white hair seemed to shine with the reflection of the joy that reigned in her heart. (For Miriam had not veiled her head since the day she left her husband, saying: the veil of a married woman becomes me ill, for I am not married.)

Miriam to Hannah Naemi: "Why these tears, Hannah Naemi? Nay, rejoice, for see, today we shall in very truth behold the day of our deliverance! My son will return from the land of bondage, as our fathers returned from Egypt!" And her hands flew to her baking as in the days of her far-off youth.

Then, as is the custom at the Passover, she set out the bed near the table very beautifully with silk cushions and rich coverlets, for on this day they say among the Jews: "Today we are once more Kings in Israel."

Miriam to Hannah Naemi: "Nay, rejoice, Hannah Naemi! For see, I am preparing my son's marriage bed as it were: today his people will lead him home as though he were a bride!"

She then prepared the meal and laid the table before the bed (but she laid not three covers, but five).

Now when Hannah Naemi saw the fourth cover she gave a loud sob, for she thought of Trophäea. But when she beheld the fifth cover, her tears stopped in alarm.

Miriam to Hannah Naemi: "Nay, rejoice, Hannah Naemi, for see, my two children are going to join us at table like bridegroom and bride!"

And so the evening of the Feast broke, on which the doors of our houses are thrown open, for at the Passover we say: "On this night none can do us injury, for it is the night when the Lord slew the enemies of Israel in the land of the Egyptians."

THE Jews of Rome relate:

When the doors were thrown open, Miriam chanted a hymn of praise over them, for she could no longer control the joy in her heart.

Miriam: "Open, O ye doors, and remain wide open like the wings of my heart! O doors that have been comforted, ye joyful doors, ye blessed doors, doors which the angel of death of the Lord passed by when he slew the first-born of our enemies in the land of Egypt! Ye doors through which the blessing of the Lord will enter Israel!"

Next she praised the thresholds of the doors, saying: "O ye thresholds that have been comforted, ye blessed thresholds, ye thresholds over which the feet of my two children will step!" And at the same time her white hairs again shone about her face with the reflection of her joy. She then sat down to the meal.

And so, that night all the doors in the Jewish city remained open. (But it was the night when Trophäea carried the Infant Jesus to Sancta Maria.)

THE Jews of Rome relate:

Thus it was that when the mob invaded our city that night—for they thought that the vanished Jewess had sought refuge with her booty among her own people—they found a free entry into all our houses, and everywhere they burst in among the sleeping inmates, exclaiming: "You vile Jews, is it not enough for you to have crucified Our Savior? Must you now rob Rome of its holy Infant Jesus that you may martyr it in your synagogues? Truly they do well who persecute you!"

Then amid threats and shoutings they began a thorough search of our houses, not hesitating at any violence whenever they thought anyone was trying to oppose them or to conceal something from them. So it happened that many of us, who with broken heads were making our escape by way of the streets, ran straight into the riders of the Frangipani who had brought the body of the dead Trophäea to the Pier Leone palace.

She lay in the light of the torches before the gate on the stones of the street, in her tattered bridal robe, the faded purple of which was luridly dyed by the red streaming from her heart. With wild lamentations our people threw themselves on their knees beside her, rousing the whole palace with their clamor, so that soon every window was filled with faces.

The servants of the palace then went to the Cardinal Pier Leone and begged him to step out on to the balcony and command quiet.

CARDINAL Pier Leone.

He was still occupied with the care of his sister Tullia. She now lay stretched upon his threshold, like the dead woman in the street below, moaning incessantly: "I am a slaughtered innocent!"

The Cardinal within him, but as if an entirely strange voice accompanied the words: "*Agnus Dei qui tollis peccata mundi, miserere nobis*—" Then, as if a curtain dropped from before a mystery: "So it is not only that our people are our cross, but the cross is also upon our people, for there is yet another way of taking on oneself the cross of Christ: to crucify Christ—"

The Cardinal to the servants (his face suddenly become ashy-pale): "I do not wish to see slaughtered innocents!"

At the same moment he heard a voice near him (he thought it was that of the silversmith, but he saw no one): "Do you understand now what I meant?"

The Cardinal trembling: "Friend, it is not the Christian you must seek, but Justice!"

The Silversmith: "Then I must make ready for another long period of wandering."

The Cardinal: "Not so long as you think. The power is mine and the hour is mine; tomorrow I shall be Pope. Then there will be no more slaughtered innocents."

The Silversmith: "And what will you do with the slaughtered Innocent on the Cross?"

At that moment the Crucifix over in the chapel fell from the wall.

FROM the archives of our golden city of Rome.

Later we all expressed our astonishment that in the course of that night the three horsemen of Antichrist had not been heard anywhere in the streets of Rome, for we have every reason to think that they must have ridden into our city on this particular night, in accordance with the solemn promise to visit us again that they had made after the black coronation of King Henry. However, the only horsemen we heard were those of the Pier Leoni who suddenly sallied forth in the middle of the night to take swift and secret possession of all the important points of our city, saying: "We are taking steps to defeat the Frangipani, for it has come to our ears that they intend to prevent our master's remains from being brought to the basilica of St. Paul where they are to find their last resting-place." Thus the whole night through the muffled sound of arms and horses was heard in all our streets as far as the Lateran Palace, so that one might have thought that Petrus Leonis was to lie in the basilica of St. John instead of in that of St. Paul. If you ask us, however, whether we are quite sure that we did not hear the horsemen of Antichrist, but only those of the Pier Leoni, we reply: we not only heard the latter, but we actually saw them, in the glare, namely, of an exceptionally hard and yellow light which issued and fell upon us first of all from the windows of the Pier Leone palace, where we stood gathered round the body of Trophäea, and afterwards from the hands of the riders themselves, in such a way that we were both struck by the light and illumined by it. For it must not be supposed that owing to the martyr's death of the Jewess at Sancta Maria on the Capitol, we were inclined that night to reject the evil reports about Cardinal Pier Leone and his family; on the contrary we said first of all: "The Cardinal is no less to blame for the death of this innocent maiden, than the fierce Frangipani. Had he received the herald these sent him in regard to her, and taken her under his protection, she would not now be lying here in her blood!" Those on the other hand who had raided the Jewish city with the Frangipani, said: "We refuse to admit for one moment that we have done wrong. You must prove to us first that this Jewess was really a martyr of the holy Infant Jesus, for we understand that she was blind. Hence it seems to us quite likely that she merely missed her way, and arrived at Sancta Maria with her booty by mistake. We see nothing Christian in that, and certainly no reason to talk about a miracle. Thus we are not in the least shaken in our conviction that the Jews like to steal our holy images and mutilate them; and as regards the Pier Leoni we shall continue to keep them at a distance until all this matter is properly cleared up."

Now when this light, of which we have just spoken, appeared in the windows of the palace and shot its sparks of gold into us so to speak, we one and all of us suddenly returned quietly to our homes, always, that is to say, following close behind the riders of the Pier Leoni. And at each step it became clearer to us, and more certain that, in spite of all the uneasy experiences we had lately been through, we still wanted our "golden Pope." And it was because of this desire that we so soon forgot the innocent death of the Jewess Trophäea. Hence to this day we say in Rome: "It was never definitely proved whether she was a daughter of God or of Satan. And so the mystery of her death lies buried in the mystery of Jesus Christ until the Day of Judgment, when all the sufferings unjustly inflicted in this world will be made manifest." But as regards the light that was scattered over us from the Pier Leone palace on the night of her death, they call it in Rome: "The payment of the thirty pieces of silver."

XIII

FROM the archives of our Golden City of Rome. We are now entering the period of the Passion of Our Lord Jesus Christ, the Passion, namely, of His mystical body, our Holy Church, which Passion is known as "the great or real Schism of the West." First then we will beat our own breast, saying at the same time: "*Agnus Dei qui tollis peccata mundi, miserere nobis!*"

We will now proceed to describe the supper of the Cardinals.

THE Supper of the Cardinals.

From the notes of the Cardinal-Bishop Petrus of Portus.

The thoughts of our brother Heimericus are hard to divine, as he takes not the slightest trouble to make them clear to us. It is a matter of indifference to him if people praise him, and he is equally indifferent if they murmur against him. And this is what many of our brothers are doing at the present moment, the reason being that he has suddenly issued an order for our Holy Father, sick unto death though he be, to be conveyed from the Lateran to the fortified monastery of Saint Andreas in Clivus Scauri. We are all strongly opposed to this idea, out of pity for our dying Pontiff and Father, for whom such a difficult journey would be attended with great suffering, not to speak of the risk he would run of expiring on the way.

But this plan also fills us with alarm because of the bad news we have lately received from Germany. There Duke Conrad of Swabia has

risen against the newly-elected King Lothair to whom our Holy Father
has promised the Imperial crown. Hence we all say to ourselves: Who
knows what our Holy Church will once again have to submit to? Our
brother Heimericus has deliberately taken it upon himself to steer the
bark of St. Peter on a sudden new course, and by this arbitrary exercise of
his powers he has plunged us all into dire uncertainty. We cannot afford
at this hour to offend the Pier Leoni, whom we have entrusted with the
protection of the conclave, by secretly withdrawing from them, for the
Church cannot dispense entirely with the support of the secular sword.
This was clearly shown in the days of the Emperor Henry.

Accordingly as the eldest of the Cardinals I presented myself before
our brother Heimericus and asked him why he had taken such an
extraordinary measure?

Whereupon he in his curt way: He had been given the order that
we were to move.

Myself: Our Holy Father lay on his death-bed and could no longer
issue orders. From whom then had he received this order?

Our brother Heimericus: He had received it from the Bishop who
had once consecrated him a Bishop of Holy Church.

Myself: Would he please explain himself more clearly.

He: There was no time for that now, as we had to move that very
night. (It was the night, however, on which the riders of the Pier Leoni
overran the whole city.) Then our brother Heimericus shut himself up in
his inexorable silence, of which we all say that it stands there like a wall
that no one can penetrate.

I reported all this to our brothers.

They were already seated at supper when I entered, as ever since our
Holy Father lay dying we had remained day and night in the Lateran
Palace, and took our meals there in common.

When I told them everything and laid before them the will of our
brother Heimericus, they all rose from their chairs as one man, exclaiming: "The Chancellor is not our master, he is only our colleague. We will
not allow our Holy Father to be dragged from his death-bed and to die

in the streets like a common thief." Thus they all raised their voices in a storm of protest against the Chancellor, who stood in the middle of them straight as a sword, and as usual opposing a blank wall of silence to their clamor.

Suddenly the door opened and our dying Father entered like an apparition from the dead: his countenance white, his hair white, his raiment white, and beneath his shoulders the white sleeves of two young priests, like two wings on which he was suspended, so to speak.

For a moment we were all struck dumb with bewilderment and terror, then: "Holy Father, what are you doing? Whom do you seek? Return to your bed! What has happened to you?"

He glanced round our circle, then in a voice so distant that it seemed already to come from the other shore, and yet at the same time broken with grief, lamenting in a way that only human beings upon earth can lament: "One of you—one of you—is about to betray Christ—"

We with renewed terror: "What do you mean, Holy Father? Whom do you mean?"

But his bright feverish eyes still travelled over our circle, passing rapidly from one to the other of us, so that his glance seemed broken in pieces like the sprung strings of an Aeolian harp. All our brothers who reside in Rome were assembled there, only our brothers from other parts were absent; of us Romans the only one not present was our brother Pier Leone; he had excused himself on account of his father's burial, which was to take place on the following morning. The broken glance of our Holy Father remained fixed on the empty place.

Suddenly we all stood in the light of that glance.

The Holy Father, still gazing at the empty chair: "He has gone out… because I am about to die…"

At that moment it was as if someone said in our hearts: "And it was night"; for they are the words one reads in the Gospel.

Now when we left the Lateran Palace to betake ourselves to Saint Andreas (secretly by the Porta Asinaria, then outside along the city wall

as far as the Porta Metronis) there was a violent downpour of rain, so
that it was as if all the heavens from North, South, East and West were
unloosed upon our little convoy at the same time. The moon coursed
through the clouds; in its uncertain light we could see through the
breaches in the walls the uncertain forms of the riders of the Pier Leoni,
and it was as if on the other side of the walls the moon were curling the
sweeping torrent into numberless vague shapes. We then put out our
torches and continued our way accompanied solely by the dark winds.

As we turned through the Porta Metronis to enter the city again—
here lay the moldering remains of the military engines with which King
Henry had assaulted the city when he rose against Pope Gregory—the
Holy Father gave a loud groan under the tent with which we had covered his litter, for our brother Heimericus kept urging the bearers to
hurry, and at almost every step they stumbled against the lumber. So
I bent down to our Holy Father and asked him if it was more than he
could bear.

He, groaning again, feebly, in the irregular rhythm of the fever-
stricken: "The sins of the world—the great sins of the world—" Then:
"Are all our brothers with us?"

Myself: "Holy Father, only those from abroad are absent."

Whereupon he: "Pray then, that none of you may yield to
temptation—"

At that moment the wind raised the flaps of the tent, so that the
cold rain lashed the face of the dying man. But just then we were passing
by the ruins known as "the ancient palace of Symmachus"; at this point
one enters the streets that had been destroyed during the fire of the Normans, and before us stretched a vista of houses one after the other a heap
of ashes, as if a wild black script ran on either side of the road. This was
the cruel sight that mocked the dying gaze of our Holy Father.

The Holy Father again: "The sins of the world—the great sins of the
world!" Then for the second time: "Pray then, that none of you may yield
to temptation!"

Suddenly I had an impulse to lay my hand on our Holy Father's

brow, so as to assure him that we were at his side. His face was wet with
the rain, and at the same time clammy like that of a man who sweats
blood in the extremity of his anguish. It seemed to me that I felt all the
distress of our Holy Church lying upon him like a stone.

In my soul (but it was in his): "Why, O Christ, dost thou not enfold
her in the wings of thy angels? Why dost Thou give Thy bride ever into
the hands of men?"

In my soul (but it was in his): "It is always the world wherever we
go; it is always the world wherever we are: always rebellion and violence,
pride and violence, money and violence, hatred and violence—"

In my soul (but it was in his): "For behold, I send you as sheep in
the midst of wolves—"

In my soul: "Holy Father, I pray that none of us may yield to
temptation."

ALL at once one of the bearers cried out: "The Holy Father is passing
away!"

As we were just passing the little church of Sancta Maria in Domnica, we went inside with the litter, in order that our Holy Father might
not die in the streets like some poor fugitive. In so far as we could find
room in the church, we knelt down beside him; the rest of us remained
in the porch, also on our knees—all save our brother Heimericus who
remained erect like a towering warrior standing on guard among the
columns. Between these the moon pursued her wandering flight.

Suddenly on the other side of the street a miserable little old woman
made a sign to us, calling out in a feeble supplicating voice: "Reverend
Fathers, hear the confession of a poor soul!"

At this one of our servants tried to get rid of her, saying: "Why, you
poor little woman, what great crime have you committed? Can you not
wait till the morning, when the others go to confession?"

She: "No, I cannot wait till the morning, when the others go to confession, for by tomorrow the great disaster will have come!"

Whereupon we: "What means this foolish talk, little woman? Are

you wanting to tell our fortunes in the manner of the Pagans? It seems
to us, you have already confessed your greatest sin."

She humbly: "Reverend Fathers, you are better judges than I of my
greatest sin. If I have already confessed that, hear then my second greatest; for it is that that brings me here."

We (for her humility touched our hearts strangely): "Well, good
woman, we will gladly hear the confession of your sin and console you
with the grace of Christ, but remain a little while in silent prayer with us,
for there is a dying man in this church."

She: "I know, yes I know, reverend Fathers, for were it not for my sin,
perhaps our Holy Father would not be dying here so miserably."

Whereupon we, in alarm because she knew who we were: "What is
this you say about the Holy Father, good woman?"

At the same time one of our servants abruptly went up to her and
scanned her face in the light of the moon. "My lords," he cried, "this is the
woman Susa whom the people call the saint of Sancta Maria de Inferno!"

We at once gathered round her, having long had a desire to see her;
but some years ago she had disappeared, and we thought she had secretly
fled from Rome because she had been denounced to us on a charge
of preaching to the people strange and scandalous doctrines about the
coming of Antichrist.

We: "Well, mother Susa, it seems to us we also know your second
sin: You have talked a great deal of nonsense."

She again, full of humility: "Reverend Fathers, you are better judges
than I of my second sin, hear then my third: that is a sin not of talking
but of silence, for of a truth no woman is called upon to speak, unless
she is ready at all times to hold her tongue for the love of Christ and
His Church!"

Suddenly the towering figure of our brother Heimericus turned to
her: "Speak then, mother Susa, tell us what has brought you here."

She, falling on her knees: "In the Name of the Father and of the
Son and of the Holy Spirit! Reverend Father, today I beheld a consecrated priest of Jesus Christ, one of your brothers, sitting on the throne

of St. Peter, at his feet the crucified Church, and above his head the sign of Antichrist; this last formed of the sins of thousands of men. This I was charged to reveal, in order that, by citing the name of him whom I beheld, I might warn the faithful of our Holy Church of Rome."

The Chancellor: "By whom were you charged with this mission, mother Susa?"

She (lowering her head): "My lord, by the grace of God."

He: "And wherefore did you not fulfill your mission?"

She: "Reverend Father, I was sent, but not authorized, and so my courage failed me."

He: "What do you mean by 'not authorized'?"

She: "I was taught in my youth that a Christian woman must keep silence."

He: "Yet in the past you have done a great deal of talking, mother Susa?"

She: "Reverend Father, so long as I did not understand that I was talking, yes I talked, but when I understood, then I held my peace. And now on the morrow's morn my vision will be fulfilled without warning! And so I deliver up my silence to Holy Church that she may judge it!"

The Chancellor: "Mother Susa, we will not judge your silence, but we authorize you to speak."

At that moment they came out of the church again with the litter, saying that the Holy Father had revived and desired to proceed further.

The Chancellor: "Come, mother Susa, rise up, and say what you have been commanded to say." But she remained on her knees.

She: "And when I have spoken, Reverend Father?"

He in a kindly voice: "Mother Susa, in eternity many will have to keep silence who have liked using their tongues in this world, but you in eternity will be allowed to keep silence. On earth, however, you too must bear your cross."

At this she sprang up exclaiming: "If I am to bear it, I will bear it with joy!" Then her voice burst forth like that of a little grey bird, and she moved into the night singing.

And her little song of faith accompanied us the whole way as far as Saint Andreas.

From the chronicle of the monastery of Saint Andreas.

No sooner had the Holy Father and his Cardinals arrived than a great mass of people swarmed up out of the darkness, having come apparently from the direction of the Lateran Palace, and we barely had time to close the gates and raise the drawbridge. After which we extinguished the lights and prepared for bed.

The mob below, however, began pulling the chains of the bridges with great violence, also making as if to leap over the moat, shouting that they knew quite well that Pope Honorius had been carried off dead from the Lateran, and that his body was now being concealed in the monastery. Accordingly in the first instance our Abbot—for we had not yet perceived that the riders of the Pier Leoni were standing behind the people with their hands full of gold—bade our lay-brother Quirinus show himself on the walls. (This brother has a ready wit, and he was told to handle the mob by bantering them in such a way that they would enjoy his jokes at their expense and disperse in laughter.)

With long strides he marched pompously up and down in the moonlight, calling down from the top of the walls that the Holy Father had just appointed him, the poor lay-brother Quirinus, to be his legate: so they would have to negotiate with him.

But they shouted back that he was a lying knave: they knew only too well that Pope Honorius would never be able to appoint another legate. But if they were wrong, let the Holy Father show himself and bless them. Otherwise they would never believe that he was still alive.

The brother on the wall, still strutting about very magnificently: This was certainly a most unusual way of petitioning the Holy Father. It was not customary to bless a raging multitude. Would they at least have the goodness to kneel down?

Whereupon a large stone whizzed past his ear.

In return the rogue on the wall threw them a fine large apple.

They: What did he take them for, did he think they were children who could be put off with fruit?

He: Well, to speak truly, he did.

They: Very well then, they would give him one of their blessings, and he could look upon it as the last he would ever receive.

At this brother Quirinus retired, and the mob prepared for the assault.

THE Cardinal-Bishop of Portus.

Meanwhile the last hour of the Holy Father Honorius had really arrived, and once more we were all gathered round him on our knees as at Sancta Maria in Domnica. Only our brother Heimericus kept apart, standing erect, as then, and eyeing the people from the open gallery.

Suddenly he stepped back and went up to the dying Pontiff: "Holy Father, the people desire your blessing."

Our dying Father (his body started convulsively at every wave of menace that rose from the raging mob below, but his mind no longer understood them) in a whispered breath: Let them give the people his blessing.

Our brother Heimericus remained still for a moment, as if he were painfully trying to collect all his strength. Then: "Holy Father, you must bestow the blessing yourself."

At this we all raised our heads and looked at him, speechless with indignation; while the Abbot of Saint Andreas who was kneeling by our Holy Father's pillow, bent over him more deeply, more prayerfully, so that the sleeve of his black cowl lay about the head of the dying man like a protecting wing.

Nevertheless our brother Heimericus for the second time (but it was as if his voice snapped in two like a staff): "Holy Father, you must bestow the blessing yourself."

But the dying man seemed not to understand.

With expiring voice, no longer the Pope Honorius, but just an ordinary mortal in the hour of his last extremity: "Pray with me—bring me the cross—"

The Chancellor, however, with his pale, inexorable voice: "Holy Father, what you are being asked for is the cross—"

Whereupon some of us murmured audibly against him: "The last moments, even of the Pope, belong to God and the soul!"

Suddenly our dying Father raised his arms with a pathetic movement towards our brother Heimericus (they dropped down at once limply to his sides): "Lift me up!"

At this the hot tears streamed from our eyes.

Then our brother Heimericus (he alone was still able to speak) called for a coverlet. It was brought, but no one dared touch the dying man in his death agony. So our brother Heimericus took him in his arms and carried him on to the gallery; but we all felt as if he were carrying out of the room the martyred body of Holy Church herself. And there our Holy Father truly hung on the arms of his Chancellor as on the tree of the Cross.

When the uproarious mob beheld the man they believed to be dead (two clerics held torches on both sides of the loggia) there was an instantaneous silence; then they all fell on their knees.

And at the same moment the heart of Pope Honorius beat its last. And now—as it seemed to us—there was only our great brother Heimericus hanging as it were on the cross of his dead master.

THE night after the death of the Holy Father Honorius II.

The Cardinal-Bishop of Portus.

I write these notes for the sake of our brother Heimericus, of whom it was afterwards said (namely by our brother Pier Leone), that he first of all carried off our dying master, then martyred him, and finally had him hurriedly put in the ground without ceremony like a malefactor. (It was with this story that our brother Pier Leone rallied the foreign Cardinals to himself and assembled them at Saint Mark's.)

The storm outside had passed over, the rain had ceased, Rome lay under a canopy of stars. From the heights of the Palatine the shimmering light of the Septemsolia Palace shone down through the blue night, breaking like waves of pearl into the room where we watched by our dead Father.

Our brother Heimericus (it seemed to us as if in this one night he had turned as grey as the old grey palace) gazing at this with a sigh: "Why do you shine, now he is dead?" (But like him we all thought of the terrible night of storm we had passed through, saying to ourselves: "Our Holy Father drained the chalice to the dregs.")

Our brother Heimericus: He knelt down by his dead master and kissed his hands, his ring, his feet, solemnly as one does the living Pope, but with great fervor and almost despairingly as if he were beseeching the dead man's pardon for all the torment of his last hour. Thus our Holy Father Honorius was Pope for one last moment after his death.

Then our brother *camerlingo* took up the silver hammer in order to do what has to be done to all Popes who have just died, before they can be declared dead. Thrice he prostrated himself on the ground, calling the deceased by his name (not indeed by the name he bore as Pope, but by the name he had received as a child in holy baptism; in this way we confess that in death all dust is equal).

Our brother Heimericus: When he heard the name pronounced, he covered his eyes with both hands, so deeply was he moved by the fact that now at last in death our Father was allowed to become an ordinary man again, when even in his dying hour he had still to remain Pope. At the same time tears streamed down his face in a way that I have never yet seen tears stream down the face of any man: and thus for the space of an hour our great brother Heimericus was also a mere man.

Meanwhile our brother *camerlingo* struck the forehead of our dead Father thrice with the silver hammer. We then prepared for his burial, for there is a law that we may not proceed to the election of a new Pope until the dead Pope has been laid in the ground.

But we had no coffin ready to hand, so once more our brother Heimericus took our dead Father in his arms and solemnly bore him down to the crypt of the church. We then began the obsequies.

When we had finished these, we prayed once again with great fervor for our absent brothers, as our dead Father had bidden us, that no one might yield to temptation (for we well knew that those who had not been with us at supper, would never understand us).

Then all of us who were present at Saint Andreas unanimously elected our brother Gregory of Saint Angelo Pope under the name of Innocent II.

By this time day had already dawned, and the golden riders of the Pier Leoni together with the people betook themselves to St. Paul's, to bury Petrus Leonis. Thus we enthroned Pope Innocent undisturbed in the basilica of Constantine. After which we took refuge again with him in Saint Andreas.

XIV

FROM the archives of our Golden City of Rome: When the funeral ceremony of Petrus Leonis at St. Paul's was over, and we of the people were making our way back to Saint Andreas (we are the same who created the uproar during the night) with light hearts and jingling pockets, for the riders of the Pier Leoni had again scattered money profusely among us, we suddenly perceived the woman Susa once more, sitting as of old in the ancient Forum of the Romans near the church of Sancta Maria de Inferno. Delighted to see her again, we rushed up to her.

"Welcome, welcome, mother Susa! It is a long time since we have seen you! Good that you are back in Rome again! God bless you always!" Then: "Well, what about Antichrist? We no longer hear any mention of him nowadays."

She: "That I can well believe, for he himself is only a poor sinner like the rest of you."

We did not relish this reply (namely her suggestion that we were poor sinners) so we quickly changed the subject.

Surrounding her: "But truly, mother Susa, you come to us just at the right moment! We want to know whether Pope Honorius, whom the Chancellor Heimericus holds captive in Saint Andreas, is still alive. Tell us what is happening there, for you can go in and out without hindrance wherever you please; we saw that at the black coronation of King Henry."

She: "Yes, indeed, things in Rome now look very much as they did then." Then: "I will tell you what you must know, but first we will all pray together."

So we fell on our knees beside her.

She: "Let us first pray for our late sovereign, the Emperor Henry in eternity, through whom our Holy Church was reduced to the last extremity of distress and desolation."

So we prayed with her for the Emperor Henry in eternity.

She continued: "Let us next pray for the Pagan nobility of our city of Rome, especially for the fierce Frangipani, who never cease to afflict and deny the love of Christ and of our Holy Church."

So we prayed with her for the Pagan nobility and for the fierce Frangipani.

She: "Let us now pray for all the people of our city of Rome, and in the first place for the avaricious, then for the ambitious, then for the violent, then for the fickle-hearted."

So we prayed with her for all the people of our city of Rome.

We, not knowing how long she might keep us praying like this, and becoming apprehensive: "Mother Susa, will you not now tell us what is going on at Saint Andreas, so that we can reply to the riders of the Pier Leoni? We must tell you that they have promised us plenty of money, if we bring them back news. And you know what pleasure it gives us to receive this."

She: "Yes, I know that you are the true children of your golden city of Rome."

At that moment a bell began to peal in the distance.

The woman Susa: "Come, I will now tell you what has happened at Saint Andreas: Pope Honorius died during the night—" Rising, and with a voice of joy: "I announce to you the *gaudium magnum*: we have a Pope! Pray with me for the Holy Father who has been elected. In this hour he has been enthroned in the basilica of Constantine."

Then she again fell on her knees. But now we all prayed with her with the greatest fervor, for we were sure that the newly-elected Pope was our "golden Pope," so firmly had we got it into our heads that this time we should have the happiness of seeing him elected.

Immediately afterwards we hurried off to the Pier Leone palace, hoping that we might still be in time to receive a little reward for our tidings.

As we drew near, however, they shouted down to us from the walls: "Hold your peace, for we already know what has happened! But run to Saint Mark's, there you will soon learn our answer!" They then threw some handfuls of gold among us so that we stood there quite dazed. (Afterwards we understood that they meant us to open our throats at Saint Mark's.)

So we proceeded to Saint Mark's.

Just as we arrived, the door of the church opened and there issued, together with a number of cardinals, a magnificently arrayed Pope, in whom we at once recognized Pier Leone. So we joined with all our might in the chorus of acclamation that rose on all sides: "Long live Pope Anacletus, who brings us the golden age! Praise to the great family of the Pier Leoni which has conferred this blessing upon us!"

FROM the archives of our golden city of Rome.

That morning the two Tusculans said to Stephanus Normannus: "In regard to all the affairs of this world, in so far as they depend solely upon our own clever and judicious management, there invariably comes a day when they collapse of themselves, and then for a while only such can maintain themselves as represent the principle of pure violence. In our view such a day has now dawned. The Pier Leoni vaunt their Pope and shine in his glory, as though he had been lawfully elected; and this is hard to endure. Nevertheless, it seems to us inadvisable to waste our efforts in opposing them, since the people, whom today we have to take into account more than is reasonable, are acclaiming their golden Pope. Let us then allow things to take their own course for a while, so as not to get mixed up in anything untoward that may happen. In this way we shall best be in a position later to represent the honor of our city of Rome as heretofore. In the meantime let Cencius and Leo Frangipane protect Pope Innocent—today at last they are in their right role for once!"

Having spoken thus they saddled their horses and quietly left the city for their castles in the Campagna.

CENCIUS and Leo Frangipane.

The handmaid Trulla relates:

Our mistress jubilantly: "Rejoice, my pretty cousins, for your hour has struck! If you now protect Pope Innocent, you can again become the paladins of Holy Church, like Petrus Leonis before you. Just follow him with brave hearts."

At these words Cencius rose slowly from the bench (for, like his brother, he was sleeping off the effects of the night on which the Jewess was killed): "Paladins of the Church—? Follow Petrus Leonis—?" In a sudden access of rage: "Have I escaped the amorous wiles of this woman, only to let her use my sword as her plaything? Paladin of the Church! I will be honest once more!" (Rushing at her like a mad dog.)

Whereupon the young Leo: "Let her be, Cencius, she is not worth your anger. But you are right, we will be honest again. What do we care about the Church? Let her settle with her two Popes herself."

They then went to the ancient temple of the goddess Rome, which lies behind their castle. They passed the whole day there among its deserted ruins; I fancy they again recited together the prayer "Sancta Roma." And so they became honest once more.

Meanwhile I remained sitting at the feet of our mistress, snuggling up to her knees, like the little Egyptian cat the Crusaders brought us; for it went to my heart to see her tear-stained face with its evil expression. Were I not the poor handmaid Trulla, I would help her with my love (for only love can bring bad-tempered people to a better frame of mind). But I am only the poor handmaid Trulla, who can do nothing in the eyes of man, but God heareth both, the poor and the rich. So I offered up a prayer in my heart for Pope Innocent, for I think he must be the true Pope, since all forsake him, as Our Lord was once forsaken.

XV

———————◆———————

THE Jews of Rome relate: All this while Miriam was sitting at the open door of the house, with Trophäea's body in her arms, around her the women of our people wailing and weeping. Miriam, however, neither wailed nor wept, but kept her lips in constant motion between her dead daughter and the open door, addressing now one and now the other.

Miriam to her dead daughter: "Oh thou blind light, how valiantly didst thou shine! Oh light that has gone out, how bright dost thou seem!"

Then to the open leaves of the door: "Oh ye festive doors, ye purple doors, oh doors besprinkled with blood…!"

Again to her dead daughter: "For behold, my daughter, thou hast become thy mother's teacher: truly, the Lord could demand his paschal lamb; and I knew it not!"

To the doors: "Oh ye sanctified doors, ye doors made firm in faith, oh doors like the doors of our people in Egypt…!"

And so it went on, hour after hour.

Now since Miriam would not let her daughter out of her arms, nor allow the door of the house to be closed, the Rabbi Nathan ben Jechiel said to Hannah Naemi: "We must rouse my daughter, for she is beginning to stiffen like the corpse in her arms."

So Hannah Naemi approached her and said: "Miriam, release your dead daughter from your arms, and take her into your heart; there you will be able to embrace her forever."

But Miriam would not release her daughter from her arms.

Miriam to Hannah Naemi: "Shall she not join with us in receiving him for whom she adorned these doors with her blood like the doors of our people in Egypt?"

Then we all realized with a shock, that Miriam believed her daughter could not have been sacrificed in vain.

THE women of the Jews relate:

Meanwhile the news that Cardinal Pier Leone had been elected Pope, had spread to the streets of the Jewish city, filling all our houses with the joyful ringing of bells.

Then the Rabbi ben Jechiel again addressed his sister saying: "We must rouse up my daughter, for it is better for a person to die of the truth which the Lord has created, than that he should continue to live on the illusions he creates for himself."

So he approached his daughter and said to her: "Yes, Miriam, the doors of our house are besprinkled with the blood of sacrifice, and the Lord will send us the angel of His consolation at the appointed time. But He will not send us your son, for see, he has been chosen Pope of the children of Edom. So shut the doors of your hope and of this house, and say with us: the ways of the Lord are inscrutable."

Miriam passed her hand over her grey hair. Then in a low voice and with the simplicity of a little child asking a question: "Father, do you really believe that?"

The Rabbi: "My child, it is not what I believe, it is an accomplished fact. Do you not hear the ringing of the bells?"

Miriam again passed her hand over her grey hair. Then suddenly springing up: "What does it mean—a fact?" And without shawl or veil or anything to cover her white hair, she made for the door.

THE women of the Jews relate:

Now when we saw that she wanted to go into the street to see what was happening, we all clung to her dress, crying: "Oh Miriam, remain here! What do you want in the streets, you poor thing, among a host of strangers?"

But she tore herself free and continued on her way, passing out through the door and making for the sound of the bells. We followed on her heels, begging and imploring her to return, and surrounding her in order to hide her from the eyes of strangers; but she kept on her way as if she were quite alone in the midst of us.

When we had left the streets of the Jewish city behind us, and were entering the ancient Forum of the Romans, we met streams of people approaching us from all sides, gaily dressed in their holiday clothes, with flowers in their hands and hymns on their lips, and calling out: "We are going to the basilica of Constantine, where Pope Anacletus is to be enthroned this very hour. We are going to greet him with shouts of acclamation; for in truth with this Pope we shall enter upon the golden age."

And now we could see the procession from St. Mark's debouching on to the Forum from the other side: in front were the golden riders of the Pier Leoni, then came the guilds of singers and the standard bearers, and then a host of golden and purple mantles and mitres, all moving across the ancient grey ruins, among which they looked like a gorgeous array of tall stately flowers bowing their heads towards us. At the same time shouts arose on all sides: "God bless Pope Anacletus! Long life to him! Honor to the great family of the Pier Leoni, from which he springs!"

But when we thus heard the name Pier Leone, we glanced at Miriam.

Suddenly she raised her voice: "Ibn Mischal, your word is fulfilled!" Then throwing herself in the way of the oncoming procession: "This man cannot be the true Pope! Listen to me, you Romans, for I am his mother, to whom it was prophesied that he would one day rend the Empire of Christendom!"

All the people round her looked at her with amazement. Then many burst out laughing, but some said to us: "Take your crazy old witch away, you Jewish women, or the riders of the Pier Leoni will trample her down!"

But Miriam continued her cry: "Listen to me! Oh listen to me! This man is not the true Pope! This man is not a Christian—he is (with a sob) my son, who has returned home to his fathers—hear what I say—he is rending Christendom!" At the same moment the golden riders of the Pier Leoni rode her down and she was flung against the wall. Then the procession of Pope Anacletus passed by us in all its splendor and amid the jubilation of the multitude. A few moments later the Forum was empty.

Suddenly it was as if the stone wall behind us started to sob: "This is all only a dream—only a dream—only a dream! Oh my children, my two dear children!" And so we also began weeping, and fell on our knees beside the weeping wall; but Miriam stood erect above us, her face turned to the streaming stone.

All at once Hannah Naemi cried out as if in mortal terror: "Miriam, do not doubt the Lord our God! Do not blaspheme!"

Miriam (turning her face away from the wall, her fists clenched like two hard stones): "Doubt the Lord our God—? Blaspheme—?"

She slowly extended her arms, and it was as if her two clenched fists were the covered scales of a balance, the needle of which was somehow suspended in the silence of our mortal terror. Then abruptly opening her left hand as if she were letting something fall, with her clenched right hand she struck herself on the forehead. And it seemed at that moment as if both her countenance and her voice broke in pieces.

Like the clatter of potsherds falling to the ground:

"Nevertheless I am always with Thee,
For Thou hast held me by my right hand!
Although my flesh and my heart hath fainted away,
Thou art the God of my heart, and the God that is my portion
     forever—"

And the mercy of God shrouded her in madness.

As though a stream surged up in her voice and flooded all its fragments: "For there is no star over the expectation of Israel, there is no spot in the world where we shall fix our home! In vain Rachel weeps for her children from generation to generation—"

As though a second wave rose over her voice: "All the mothers of the world weep for their children! For behold Israel is their image for evermore: all the pitchers of hope draw up death at the last—"

Again we heard the shouts in the distance: "Long live Pope Anacletus! Justice and happiness for all men!"

(The third wave over Miriam's voice.)

With the surging tones of an organ: "Oh, almighty sorrow!" (Her eyes wide open, as if she beheld an apparition): "Oh, all-victorious sorrow!" (Taking two steps forward): "Oh, all-ruling, all-conquering sorrow!" (As if forced back against the wall.)

Then to the other side, again as if advancing towards an apparition: "Oh almighty sorrow—Oh all-victorious sorrow!" (Again turning back.) "Oh all-ruling, all-conquering sorrow—"

And for the third time she moved round in a circle, turning in every direction as if she were looking for a way out and found herself confronted on all sides by the same apparition.

And then again and again.

Meanwhile darkness was slowly spreading around us.

Suddenly we saw a host of little birds flying over the city of Rome, scurrying with cries of alarm and a great flapping of wings, over the walls into the open country beyond. We thought at first that the darkness that was descending upon us came from the clouds of these countless little birds. But soon the trees above us on the Palatine also became uneasy and began to sigh and groan (yet there was not a breath of wind).

And now people came hurrying back in swarms from the Lateran, terrified like the birds and the trees, and calling out: "It is the night of St. Peter, which also descended upon us at the black coronation of King Henry; it began the very moment that they installed Pope Anacletus in the basilica of Constantine on the holy throne of the Pope."

And always it grew darker and darker.

A few of the crowd came up to us, saying: "Is not that the woman who exclaimed just now that Pope Anacletus was not the true Pope? Mark ye, this may be one of the signs of this alarming day!"

They then formed a circle with us round Miriam.

All this while she had kept turning this way and that, with eyes wide open, but unafraid, her countenance now, and not only her voice, entirely submerged in the vast, strange wave. Gradually fainter and fainter, already dead to all memory, almost inwardly: "Oh almighty sorrow—oh all-victorious sorrow—oh all-redeeming sorrow—" (Falling down dead.)

It was now blackest night.

FROM the archives of our golden city of Rome.

Suddenly in the middle of our group a woman cried out: "Let us do penance for our sins, for truly this dead woman here beheld the cross of Christ over the city of Rome."

At the word "cross" the Jewish women took fright and dispersed hastily. Then we recognized beside us the woman Susa standing before her little house in the darkness.

Trembling we addressed her (she was at that moment laying her shawl under the dead woman's head): "Mother Susa, tell us, what does all this that is happening signify?"

She, without fear, almost gaily: "It signifies that you shall all be saved through this great Schism which rends the body and the love of our Holy Church."

Whereupon the rest of us weeping bitterly: "Mother Susa, help us to understand! How can it be that we shall be saved through so great a calamity?"

The woman Susa: "This is how you shall understand." (Kneeling down in the darkness.) "Fold your hands and say: 'We adore thee, O Jesus Christ, for by Thy Cross Thou hast redeemed the whole world.'"

CONCLUSION

HERE we record the conclusion. This took place on the day which is known in Rome as the Good Friday of the great Schism, in other words on the day when Pope Anacletus rent the unity of Holy Church, which is the love of Christ among us, and as it were nailed it upon the Cross. On the following day his golden riders drove our Holy Father Innocent into flight; thus in the grey dawn of that day, the new unity of our Holy Church was mysteriously taken from its dark tomb in our city of Rome, out into the great Church of Christendom like a beautiful Paschal candle. And so we call this day the Holy Saturday of the great Schism. Afterwards the whole of Christendom was slowly ignited by the candle of this new unity: first of all the land of France, where the holy Abbot Bernard of Clairvaux seized its fire; then the land of Germany where the warring hosts of Duke Conrad of Swabia and King Lothair felt their hearts kindle to love in its flame. And thus all the world over, people became converted and reconciled. Then with one accord they rose, the Saint from France and the King from Germany, and set out for Rome to restore Pope Innocent, the two of them preceded by the sacred sword of the Emperor of Christendom. (All the people of Rome received them with rejoicings.) And so the day of their arrival is known as the day of Pentecost of the great Schism; on this day was fulfilled, through the Spirit of Love, what the woman Susa had previously announced to us when she told us that we should all be saved through this great calamity.

Hence it is that we in no wise curse Pope Anacletus, but, whenever we speak of him, we repeat each time the holy words of the Liturgy: "*O felix culpa.*"

WE have still to relate of Pope Anacletus.

Now when King Lothair was about to be crowned Emperor of Christendom, and they were making ready to drive away the golden riders of Pope Anacletus (these still stood entrenched in St. Peter's, his last stronghold), they first went to the Holy Father Innocent, to ask him: "What shall we do to Pope Anacletus, if we capture him?"

Whereupon the Holy Father Innocent: "You shall do to him nothing, but you shall put to him the question of Pope Paschal, for this still remains unanswered."

They then proceeded to the fortress of St. Peter's.

But when they arrived there, there was not a single golden rider to be seen anywhere, and all the doors stood open; they went from room to room, but nowhere could they find Pope Anacletus. Accordingly they reported to the Holy Father Innocent that Pope Anacletus had departed.

The Holy Father Innocent: "Very well then, let someone set out after him with the question of Pope Paschal."

It was the aged Bishop Petrus of Portus who subsequently set out on this mission, but at the time of our writing he has not yet returned, and so the question of Pope Paschal still follows Pope Anacletus to this day.

FINIS

CLUNY MEDIA

Designed by Fiona Cecile Clarke, the CLUNY MEDIA *logo
depicts a monk at work in the scriptorium,
with a cat sitting at his feet.*

*The monk represents our mission to emulate
the invaluable contributions of the monks
of Cluny in preserving the libraries of the West,
our strivings to know and love the truth.*

*The cat at the monk's feet is Pangur Bán, from the
eponymous Irish poem of the 9th century.
The anonymous poet compares his scholarly
pursuit of truth with the cat's happy hunting of mice.
The depiction of Pangur Bán is an homage to the work
of the monks of Irish monasteries and a sign
of the joy we at Cluny take in our trade.*

"Messe ocus Pangur Bán,
cechtar nathar fria saindan:
bíth a menmasam fri seilgg,
mu memna céin im saincheirdd."

Made in the USA
Middletown, DE
05 April 2021

37058165R10139